RESPONSIBILITIES

Some of the requirements of persons doing electrical wiring are as follows:

THE ELECTRICAL CONTRACTOR

CLASS C — 200 amps, 300 volts, single phase.

He may do minor repairs and alterations or additions to larger installations, provided he does not work on any part of an installation which exceeds the above limits.

Cost of official Examination — $25.00
Cost of Certificate — $20.00

The Government Examiner will supply you with an official code book, set of bulletins and regulations, paper etc. for you to use in writing the exam paper. Do not bring your own. Just bring pen and pencil, a slide rule or calculator.

The Electrical Contractor must:

— obtain permits for all of his work.
— not work under a permit issued to the owner or another Contractor.
— not take out a permit for work done by someone else.
— not hire uncertified men on a job basis to work under his certificate. (these men are then really contracting without a Certificate of Competency).
— do all work according to code.
— not undertake to do work which exceeds his certification.
— make sure that all electrical equipment is properly certified by CSA before it is connected.
— declare in writing to the Electrical Inspector when the work is ready for inspection.

THE STUDENT

The student who will familiarize himself with the information contained in this book should be able to write successfully the official Government examination for a Class C Certificate of Competency. Try the sample examination at the end of this book.

The student should understand that he must:

— be at least 18 years old.
— have a minimum 4 years experience in the installation and maintenance of electrical equipment or have special training satisfactory to the Chief Inspector before he may write the official exam.
— Documentary proof is required by the Chief Inspector. This may consist of a Certificate of Achievement from a training school, i.e. apprenticeship certificate or letters from employers stating level of responsibility and training received.
— obtain at least 60% on the official examination.
— If he fails the exam, he must wait 30 to 90 days before he may write again. This depends on his mark on the exam.
— If he has successfully passed the official examination he is issued a Certificate of Competency. This means he can now operate as an Electrical Contractor, but don't forget, each city or municipality he works in will want to sell him a Contractors Licence — for a fee of course.

— One more thing — after hours of study and agony over the exam, you face the Inspector in the field with each installation you do. If your work is good and your cooperation is good, you will have no problem. If it is not good, the Board of Examiners may want to talk to you about it — may even want to suspend your Certificate for a period of time.
— After two failures, it appears the thing to do is to become interested in some other trade.

THE HOMEOWNER

The homeowner must:

- obtain an electrical permit for all electrical work done, including the wiring for ranges, dryers, furnace, extra outlets, etc.
  The rules require an electrical permit for any additional wiring, any alteration, and any new wiring. It is like a building permit, it permits the holder to install certain electrical wiring and equipment in his own home. This permit must be obtained **before** any electrical work is begun.
- do all the work himself — he may not allow anyone to do any of the work covered by the permit issued to him.
  An owner may do the wiring in his own home only. This is the basis on which a permit is issued to an owner. He may not install the wiring, any wiring, in his own building if it is to be rented or sold. He may obtain an electrical permit only for his own personal dwelling. He must do all the work himself. No one, other than his immediate family, such as a father, brother, son, may do any of the electrical work under this permit. It has nothing to do with payment for work done. Even an Electrical Contractor could not work under a permit issued to an owner. Treat it as you would your drivers licence.
- do all the work according to the electrical code.
- notify, in writing, the Electrical Inspector when the work is ready for inspection. Do not request an inspection before you are, in fact, ready. The Inspector may charge a re—inspection permit fee.
- complete the entire installation including all fixtures, switches, plates, etc. before he may have a final certificate of approval.

C.S.A. CERTIFICATION

The C.S.A. monogram is your assurance that the electrical device meets certain minimum standards. This is important for any electrical device from a wall switch to the hair dryer to the electric range, all must bear this label of certification. It may be tempting to pick up that cheap light fixture in Mexico, or that under the counter electrical gizmo, whatever it is. Don't do it, it may be a fire hazard or a shock hazard. Always look for that CSA monogram. If you don't find it on the electrical device bring it to the attention of the store manager.

ELECTRICAL INSPECTIONS — WHEN TO CALL FOR INSPECTION.

ROUGH WIRING INSPECTION

Before calling for the rough wiring inspection make sure that:

1. the electrical service equipment is in place. The service conduit or cable, the meter base, service panel and the service grounding cables should all be installed for the rough wiring inspection.

    Note If you are using service **conduit**, not cable, the conductors need not be installed but the conduit must be in place.

2. all branch circuit cables are in place and properly strapped and protected from driven nails. Don't forget, all joints, splices and ground wire connection to boxes must be completed as far as possible.

    Avoid Costly Rejections and Delays.

    Before calling for the rough wiring inspection check your work very carefully as an Inspector would do his inspection. Check every detail. If you have followed the instructions in this book you should do well.

    Caution - Do not cover any wiring, not even with insulation, until it has been inspected and approved for covering.

Note - In some rural areas a sketch map may be necessary to help the Inspector find your premises. Also, if a key is required, provide instructions where to find it.

FINAL INSPECTION

1. Your installation must be complete. It's a good idea to check it carefully as an Inspector would do his inspection. Use this book as you go through your installation to check off each item. Look for forgotten or unfinished parts. Check for such things as circuit breaker ratings, tie-bars, circuit directory, grounding connections etc.. Look for open KO holes and outlet boxes. Don't forget, if any of the appliances such as a dish washer is not going in just yet you must terminate the supply cable in a fixed j-box with cover until that appliance is actually installed.

Electrical Permit - Check also if your permit covers all you have installed.

The Inspector is one of the good guys. His concern is that your installation is safe and that it meets minimum code requirments. That is, after all, exactly what you want.

ELECTRICAL INSPECTION OFFICES

District Inspectors may be reached by telephone daily from 8:30 a.m. to 9:30 a.m. only, except for those days they are inspecting in outlying areas.

Abbotsford .... **Tel 852-5270**
33780 Laurel St. V2S 1X4

Ashcroft .... **Tel. 453-2433**
4th Street & Brink Box 820, V0K 1A0

Campbell River .... **Tel. 286-7653**
1180 Ironwood St. V9W 5P7

Chilliwack .... **Tel. 795-8403**
45904 Victoria Ave. V2P 2T1

Courtnay .... **Tel. 334-1222**
941 E. England Ave. V9N 2N7

Cranbrook .... **Tel. 426-1277**
207: 107, 117 - 10th.Ave.S., V1C 2N1

Dawson Creek .... **Tel. 784-2380**
310 Prov. Build.,1201 - 103rd. Ave., V1G 4J2

Duncan .... **Tel. 746-1324, Local 222**
238 Government St., V9L 1A5

Fort St. John .... **Tel. 787-3230**
10600 - 100th. St., V1J 4L6

Kamloops .... **Tel. 828-4530**
440, 546 St. Paul St. V2C 5T1

Kelowna .... **Tel. 861-7313**
1913 Kent Rd., V1Y 7S6

Langley .... **Tel. 530-7107**
20423 Douglas Cres. Box 3092, V3A 4R3

Merritt .... **Tel. 378-9376**
110, 2025 Granit Ave. Box 3030, V0K 2V0

Mission .... **Tel. 826-2197**
32818 Seventh Ave., V2V 2C3

Nanaimo .... **Tel. 755-2320**
190 Wallace St. V9R 1M7

Nelson .... **Tel. 354-6544**
310 Ward St., V1L 5S4

New westminster .... **Tel. 660-8660**
101, 237 E. Columbia St., V3L 3W4

100 Mile House .... **Tel. 395-5500**
272 Fifth St. Box 7000, V0K 2E0

Parksville .... **Tel. 248-5311**
103, 182 W.Harrison, Box 759, V0R 2S0

Penticton .... **Tel. 492-1330, Messages 392-3109**
3547 Skaha Lake Rd. V2A 7K2

Port Alberni .... **Tel. 724-9200**
Courthouse, 4515 Elizabeth St. V9Y 6L5

Powell River .... **Tel. 485-2524**
6953 Alberni St. V8A 2B8

Prince George .... **Tel. 565-6105**
4th. Fl., Plaza 400, 1011 Fourth Ave.
V2L 3H9

Prince Rupert .... **Tel. 627-0417, G/A 627-0415**
Courthouse, V8J 1B7

Quesnel .... **Tel. 992-4240, G/A 992-4301**
206, 350 Barlow Ave., V2J 2C1

Revelstoke .... **Tel. 837-7675**
518 Second St. W. Box 1700, V0E 2S0

Richmond .... **Tel. 270-9477**
148, 10451 Shellbridge Way, V6X 2W8

Salmon Arm .... **Tel. 832-1688**
121 Hudson St. NE, Box 636, V0E 2T0

Sechelt .... **Tel. 885-5616**
102 Toredo Sq. Box 950, V0N 3A0

Smithers .... **Tel. 847-7202**
Govt. Build. Bag 5000, V0J 2N0

Squamish .... **Tel. 892-3221**
Box 1008, 38152 2nd Ave, V0N 3C0

Terrace .... **Tel. 638-3265**
4548 Lakelse Ave., V8G 1P8

Trail .... **Tel. 364-0552**
Fed. Build. 835 Spokane St. V1R 3W4

Vanderhoof .... **Tel. 567-9077**
Prov. Build. Box 1369, V0J 3A0

Vernon .... **Tel. 549-5525**
3407 - 31st. Ave., V1T 2H6

Victoria .... **Tel. 479-8225**
4248 Glanford Ave., V8Z 4B8

Williams Lake .... **Tel. 398-4481**
540 Borland Ave., V2G 1R8

The following cities and district municipalities administer their own electrical inspection service:

Corp. of Burnaby .... **Tel. 294-7130**
W.J.Malcolm, Supervisor
Office Hrs. 11:15 a.m. to 12:00 p.m.
4949 Canada Way, V5G 1M2

Corp. of Maple Ridge **Tel. 463-5221**
G.Mysel, Inspector
Office Hrs. 8:30 to 9:15 a.m. & 3:30 to 4:30 p.m.
11995 Haney Place, V2X 6G2

City of New West. .... **Tel. 521-3711**
A Pietracupa, Inspector
Office Hrs. 8:30 to 9:30 a.m., 1 to 2:00 p.m., & 3:30 to 4:30 p.m.
511 Royal Ave, V3L 1H9

Dist. of N. Van. **Tel.984-4161**
P.S.Knight, Chief Inspector
Office Hrs. 8:30 to 10 a.m. & 4 to 4:30 p.m.
355 W. Queens Rd. V7N 2K6

City of N. Van. .... **Tel. 985-7761**
A.W.Horwell, Chief Inspector
Office Hrs. 8:30 to 9:30 a.m., 1 to 2 p.m., & 4 to 4:30 p.m.
141 W. 14th. St. V7M 1H9

Municipality of Surrey **Tel. 591-4240**
D.MacIntyre, Chief Inspector
Office Hrs. 8:30 to 9 a.m. & 4:00 to 4:30 p.m.
14245 - 56th. Ave., V3W 1J2

City of Vancouver ..... **Tel. 873-7601**
D.Jackson, Chief Inspector
Office Hrs. 11:15 to 12 & 1 to 1:45 p.m.
453 W. 12th. Ave., V5Y 1V4

City of Victoria .... **Tel. 385-5711, Local 342**
M.Schwartz, Chief Inspector
Office Hrs. 8;30 to 10 a.m. & 1 to 2 p.m.
1 Centennial Square, V8W 1P6

Mun. of W. Van. ..... **Tel. 922-1211**
H.F.Lindsay, Chief Inspector
Office Hrs. 8:30 to 9:30 a.m. & 4 to 4:30 p.m.
750 - 17th. St., V7V 3T3

CONTENTS

1. SERVICE SIZE – Rule 8–200

We must begin with the electrical service box. It may appear to be very difficult to install a new electrical service in your house but it need not be so. If you read these instuctions carefully it should be easy and enjoyable and what's more, you should save a bundle.

The rules permit a service as large as we like but not as small as we like. There is a definite minimum size we must have if it is going to be passed by the Inspector.

Service size is based on two things.

A. Calculated Load – This is the sum of all the loads after certain demand factors are applied. As shown below, for an average 90 m² (968 sq.ft.) house with electric range and dryer but with gas or oil heating, the service demand load is usually between 50 and 60 amperes. Electric heating loads can raise this to 100 amps or more.

B. Minimum Service Size – This is based on floor area.

60 amp. – for any house with **less than** 80 m² (861 sq.ft.) floor area. This includes the areas of all the floors except the basement. Basement floor area is ignored completely for this purpose.

100 amp. – for any house with 80 m² (861 sq. ft.) or more floor area. As above, this includes all floors except basement.

Note – Even if the actual load is, say 30 amps, the minimum size service permitted is 100 amps if the floor area is 80 m² or more. This extra capacity is for future load.

The following table has been developed to simplify the service size calculation. The table shows a progressive load – in other words, any service size given in any column assumes all the loads shown above that value are going to be used.

For example, a 90 m² (no basement) house with **no** electical appliances such as a range, dryer, water heater or electric heating would require a 100 amp service. The material required for this service is listed under B, page 2.

If the 90 m² no basement house had a range, dryer, water heater and 15 kw. electric hot water boiler the service size would need to be minimum 117.1 amps. The material required for this service is listed under C, page 2.

Once you have determined the correct list of material for your house, measure the lengths required for your job. You can use this list when shopping for the materials you will require.

LISTS of MATERIALS

Note – Remember you need twice as much hot conductor length as neutral conductor.

A Service Size – 60 amps.   Note – may be used only if floor area above ground is **less** than 80 m² (861 sq. ft.).

    Service switch, fuse or breaker rating ––– 60 amps.
    Hot conductors –––––––––––––––– 2 – #6 R90 copper (black, red or blue)
    Neutral conductor–––––––––––––– 1 – #6R90 copper (white)
    Service conduit –––––––––––––––– 1 inch.
        or use #6 copper Teck cable.
    Meter base rating––––––––––––––– 100 amps.
    Service grounding conductor –––––––– #6 (or larger) bare copper.
    Service panel size ––––––––––––– 16 circuits (minimum)

B Service Size – 100 amps.

    Service switch, fuse or breaker rating ––– 100 amps.
    Hot conductors –––––––––––––––– 2 – #3 R90 copper (black, red or blue)
    Neutral conductor–––––––––––––– 1 – #6 R90 copper (white)
    Service conduit –––––––––––––––– 1 inch.
        or use #3 copper Teck cable.
    Meter base rating––––––––––––––– 100 amps.
    Service grounding conductor –––––––– #6 (or larger) bare copper.
    Service panel size ––––––––––––– 24 circuits.

> **Note** This panel may supply a central electric furnace, an electric boiler or baseboard heaters.

C Service Size – 120 Amps.

    Service switch, fuse or breaker rating ––– 125 amps.
    Hot conductors –––––––––––––––– 2 – #2 R90 copper (black, red or blue)
    Neutral conductor–––––––––––––– 1 – #6 R90 copper (white)
    Service conduit –––––––––––––––– 1¼ inch.
        or use #2 copper Teck cable.
    Meter base rating––––––––––––––– 200 amp.
    Service grounding conductor –––––––– #6 (or larger) bare copper
    Service panel size ––––––––––––– 24 circuits

> **Note** This panel may supply a central electric furnace or electric boiler. If heating is with electric baseboards you will need more than 24 branch circuits, see list D below.

D Same as C above except:

    Service Panel Size – 30 circuits.

> **Note** This panel may supply a central electric furnace, an electric boiler or electric baseboard heaters.

E   Service Size — 150 Amps.

Service switch, fuse or breaker rating — — —   150 amps.
Hot conductors — — — — — — — — — — — —   2 — #1/0 R90 copper (black, red or blue)
Neutral conductor — — — — — — — — — —   1— #4 R90 copper (white)
Sevice conduit — — — — — — — — — — —   1¼ inch.
      or use #1/0 copper Teck cable.
Meter base rating — — — — — — — — — —   200 amp.
Service grounding conductor — — — — — —   #4(or larger) bare copper
Service panel size — — — — — — — — — —   30 circuits

Note This panel may supply a central electric furnace or electric boiler. If heating is with electric baseboards you will need more than 30 branch circuits, see list F below.

F   Same as E above except:

Service Panel Size — 40 circuits.

Note This panel may supply central electrical furnace, an electric boiler or baseboard heaters.

G   Service Size — 200 Amps.

Service switch, fuse or breaker rating — — —   200 amps.
Hot conductors — — — — — — — — — — — —   2 — #3/0 R90 copper (black, red or blue)
Neutral conductor — — — — — — — — — —   1 — #3 R90 copper (white)
Service conduit — — — — — — — — — — —   1½ inch.
      or use #3/0 copper Teck cable.
Meter base rating — — — — — — — — — —   200 amps.
Service grounding conductor — — — — — —   #3 (or larger) bare copper.
Service panel size — — — — — — — — — —   30 circuits.

Note This panel may supply a central electric furnace or electric boiler. If heating is with electric **baseboards** the 30 circuit panelboard is too small. You will need to install a **40 circuit** panelboard.

NOTES   NOTES   NOTES

The above lists give the minimum panel size required by code in each case, however, this may not be enough for your installation. Make sure that you have a sufficient number of circuit spaces available in your panel.

See also under (b) "How Many Circuits Do I Need", on page 29.

Caution — The above lists of material are based on a literal interpretation of rule 4—022, which permits a reduced size service neutral conductor. While there is general agreement in the electrical trade, that a full size neutral conductor is wasteful because it cannot possibly ever be used, there is disagreement on how much reduction should be permitted. For this reason you should consult your local Inspector if he will accept a reduced neutral conductor.

The following explanation will help the student understand the basis of the above lists of material.

Consider the following:

It is argued 8—200 specifies a minimum size for **service** conductors for residences and the point is stressed that this includes the neutral therefore, as the argument goes, we may not reduce the neutral below the minimum size stated in that rule. It should be noted that almost the same words are used in rules 8—202, 8—204, 8—206, 8—208. Each of these rules deals with different buildings and each states "the minimum ampacity of service conductor" may not be smaller than permitted in that rule. In each case the "service conductors" includes the neutral therefore, as the argument goes, we may not apply rule 4—022 in any of those cases either. The effect of this interpretation is that we may never reduce the neutral conductor for any service. In fact, most of these rules refer to both the **service** and the **feeder** conductors. Because the neutral is a "feeder conductor" this interpretation of the rule would, therefore, not permit it's size to be reduced **under any conditions.**

It should be noted that one of the basic rules of interpretation is that a specific rule supercedes a general rule. Rule 4—022 is such a specific rule. Rule 8—200 is specific in that it refers to "service conductors" as opposed to "branch circuit conductors" but rule 4—022 is more specific in that it refers to the **neutral** only. Then notice, it refers to the neutral conductor in the **service.** It should also be noted that this rule does not limit the application to commercial buildings nor does it limit in any way, the application of this rule to services above 100 amperes only. Rule 4—022 says we do not need a full size neutral in a residential service. It must be large enough to carry all the load **connected** to the neutral. This load must be determined by the minimum demands required by rule 8—200.

In a residence the loads connected to the neutral consist of lights, plugs, and in some cases a few range cooking top elements. The oven, electric heating, dryer, water heater and sauna loads are **all NOT connected** to the neutral. All that is left is the basic load which is 5 kw for a 968 sq. ft. house. This is 20.8 amps. Therefore, according to code, the connected load on the neutral in this house is 20.8 amps.. The smallest size neutral conductor specified in the above lists is #6. A #6 R90 copper conductor may carry 65 amps. This leaves 65 — 20.8 = 44.2 amps. **spare** neutral capacity. Even if we added the 12kw range, and it would be incorrect to do so because it is not connected to the neutral, the service neutral load would still be **less** than the #6 R90 service neutral conductor could handle. The important thing to remember is that the neutral must be the same size as the service grounding conductor. Don't waste your money on a full size neutral and conduit when it is simply not possible to ever use it in a residence. Spend your money on things that can be used such as a few more outlets on the kitchen counter.

Service Size Table – For HOME OWNERS USE

The table gives the minimum service ampacity required in each case.
The letter after each ampere rating indicates which list of materials to use.

Connected load	Less than 80 m² on main floor only. (861 sq. ft.) — NO basement house	Less than 80 m² — With any size basement	80 m² up to & including 90 m² (969 sq. ft.) on main floors only. — no basement house	80 m² up to & including 90 m² — With any size basement	More than 90 m² up to & including 180 m² (1937 sq. ft.) See notes 2 & 5	More than 180 m² up to & including 270 m² (2906 sq. ft.) See note 2	More than 270 m² up to & including 360 m² (3875 sq. ft.) See note 2
Basic load only See note 3	60 amps. A	60 amps. A	100 amps. B	100 amps. B	100 amps. B	100 amps. B	100 amps. B
plus range (up to 12 kw rating)	60 amps. A	60 amps. A	100 amps. B	100 amps. B	100 amps. B	100 amps. B	100 amps. B
and 4 kw. dryer	60 amps. A	60 amps. A	100 amps. B	100 amps. B	100 amps. B	100 amps. B	100 amps. B
and 3 kw water heater See note 8	60 amps. A	60 amps. A	100 amps. B	100 amps. B	100 amps. B	100 amps. B	100 amps. B
and electric heating							
hot air furnace **or** hot water boiler — 10 kw	96.1 amps. B	100.3 amps. B	96.1 amps. B	100.3 amps. B	100.3 amps. B	*104.5 amps. C	108.6 amps. C
15	117.1 amps. C	*121.3 amps. E	117.1 amps. C	*121.3 amps. E	*121.3 amps. E	*125.5 amps. E	129.6 amps. E
18	130.1 amps. E	134.3 amps. E	130.1 amps. E	134.3 amps. E	134.3 amps. E	138.5 amps. E	142.6 amps. E
20	138.1 amps. E	142.3 amps. E	138.1 amps. E	142.3 amps. E	142.3 amps. E	146.5 amps. E	150.6 amps. E
24			*156.1 amps. G	160.3 amps. G	160.3 amps. G	164.5 amps. G	168.6 amps. G
27			169.1 amps. G	173.3 amps. G	173.3 amps. G	177.5 amps. G	181.6 amps. G
30					185.3 amps. G	189.5 amps. G	193.6 amps. G
or Baseboard heaters — Sum of all heater ratings (For sauna see note 10.) — 4 kw	69.8 amps. B	100 amps. B	100 amps	100 amps. B	100 amps. B	100 amps. B	100 amps. B
5	74.0 amps. B	100 amps. B	100 amps	100 amps. B	100 amps. B	100 amps. B	100 amps. B
6	78.1 amps. B	100 amps. B	100 amps	100 amps. B	100 amps. B	100 amps. B	100 amps. B
7	82.3 amps. B	100 amps. B	100 amps	100 amps. B	100 amps. B	100 amps. B	100 amps. B
8	86.5 amps. B	100 amps. B	100 amps	100 amps. B	100 amps. B	100 amps. B	100 amps. B
9	90.6 amps. B	100 amps. B	100 amps	100 amps. B	100 amps. B	100 amps. B	*103.1 amps. D
10	94.8 amps. B	100 amps. B	100 amps. B	100 amps. B	100 amps. B	*103.1 amps. B	107.3 amps. D
11	97.9 amps. B	*102.1 amps. B	100 amps. B	*102.1 amps. D	*102.1 amps. D	106.3 amps. D	110.4 amps. D
12	*101.0 amps. D	*105.2 amps. D	*101 amps. D	*105.2 amps. D	*105.2 amps. D	109.4 amps. D	113.5 amps. D
13	*104.2 amps. D	108.3 amps. D	*104.2 amps. D	108.3 amps. D	108.3 amps. D	112.5 amps. D	116.7 amps. D
14	107.3 amps. D	111.5 amps. D	107.3 amps. D	111.5 amps. D	111.5 amps. D	115.6 amps. D	119.8 amps. D
15	110.4 amps. D	114.6 amps. D	110.4 amps. D	114.6 amps. D	114.6 amps. D	118.8 amps. D	*122.9 amps. E
16	113.5 amps. D	117.7 amps. D	113.5 amps. D	117.7 amps. D	117.7 amps. D	*121.9 amps. E	126.0 amps. F
17	116.7 amps. D	*120.8 amps. E	116.7 amps. D	*120.8 amps. E	*120.8 amps. E	125.0 amps. E	129.2 amps. F
18	119.8 amps. D	124.0 amps. E	119.9 amps. D	124.0 amps. E	124.0 amps. E	128.1 amps. F	132.3 amps. F
19	*122.9 amps. E	127.1 amps. F	*122.9 amps. E	127.1 amps. F	127.1 amps. F	131.3 amps. F	135.4 amps. F
20	126.0 amps. F	130.2 amps. F	126.0 amps. F	130.2 amps. F	130.2 amps. F	134.4 amps. F	138.5 amps. F

NOTES

(1) Remember, this **table** gives the **minimum** sizes permitted. Services of higher rating may be installed and sometimes may be an advantage for future load additions.

(2) The floor areas in all these columns include the floor area of an in−house garage but does not include an open carport. Calculate your floor area by adding the basement floor area at 75% and the other floor areas at 100%.

(3) **Basic load** − This includes:
   − all lighting outlets
   − all 15 amp plug outlets
   − hot air furnace (standard) gas or oil burning type.
   − any appliance of less than 1500 watts (this is the same as 12.5 amps at 120 volts) each, such as a garburator, freezer, toaster, etc. but does not include fixed electric heating.

(4) * Some amperages shown on the table are marked with an asterisk. This means that the next size smaller service **may** be acceptable in this case **by special permission.** Please note this special permission is not automatic − you must request it from your local Inspector and he may refuse it if he thinks it too small, rule 8−106(1). In any case, it is not likely you will be permitted to use a smaller branch circuit panel.

(5) For example, if the floor area is 90.1 m^2 we must use this column.

(6) The table may not show the exact rating of your electrical load − in that case you may take the next size larger or calculate in detail, as described below.

(7) **Motor loads** − Hot air and hot water heating systems require motors to circulate the heat. These motors are small, they require approx. 7 amps at 120 volts. This **is included** in the values given in the table.

(8) **6 kw Water Heater** − For domestic hot water use only. It does not include an electric water heater for a hot tub or spa. Most water heater tanks are equipped with 2 − 3 kw heater elements. While this is 6000 watts in total, the switching arrangement in the thermostat is such that only one 3 kw element is working at any one time. It is a flip−flop switching arrangement. Under normal water use the lower 3 kw element will heat the water. When the demand for hot water becomes too great for the lower element the thermostat disconnects the lower heater element and connects only the upper heater element. The upper element will heat the water in only the top part of the tank, this provides rapid recovery of hot water. When the demand for hot water decreases the thermostat will switch to the lower heater element again.

(9) **7600 Watt Water Heaters** − There is a new energy saving tank available. It has 2 − 3800 watt heater elements, total wattage is 7600. With the flip−flop thermostat, as described above, the maximum load on this tank is 3800 watts. This is 800 watts more than allowed for in the table. For service calculations we add only 25% of this 800 watts. The additional load is only 200 watts. In an exam this is important − even this little bit − but on the job − well, it's not even one ampere more.

   Swimming pool, hot tub or spa - Electrical water heaters for these loads are **not** included in the table. These must be added at 100% of their rating, Rule 8-200(1)(v).

(10) **Sauna** − Rule 62−102(k) says this is considered electric heating. This load must therefore be added as electric baseboard heating. If you are using gas or oil (not electricity) to heat your house, then you may enter the table with the kw rating of the sauna heater. For example, if you are installing a 4.5 kw sauna, you would enter the table at 5 kw − see lower left corner of the table, under baseboard heaters.

   If you are using electric baseboard heaters, then simply add the sauna kw load to the total baseboard heater load before you enter the table.

(11) **Built−in Vacuum Cleaning System** − Most of these systems will draw 12.5 amps or less at 120 volts. In that case **they are included in the basic load** shown in the table. Those units which draw more than 12.5 amps at 120 volts must be added at 25% of their rating but remember to take only **half** of the amperage because the service is calculated at 240 volts. For example, if your service should be 125 amp according to the above table and you want to add a 14.0 amp vacuum cleaner system, it would look like this:

   Other load .... = 125.00 amps.

   Vacuum system .... 25% of 14 ÷ 2 = 0.25 × 7 =   1.75 amps.

   _____

   Total = 126.75 amps.

   Hardly worth the effort but it could mean that the next size larger service conductors may need to be used.

Now we know the service ampacity.

Next step, refer to table of materials on page 2.

DETAILED CALCULATION FORM — for student use.

Use the following format. Fill in the blanks as required to describe your installation. This calculation gives the minimum size service required. Then refer to the appropriate table of materials on page 2.

Step 1   <u>**Basic Load**</u> — Rule 8–200(1)

1st. 90 m^2 floor area .... =   5000 watts
next 90 m^2 floor area or portion thereof .....(Add 1000 watts) .... = _____ watts
next 90 m^2 floor area or portion thereof .....(Add 1000 watts) .... = _____ watts

Note (1)   Floor area in this case must include 75% of the basement floor area plus 100% of all other living floor areas.

Note (2)   This **basic load** includes all lighting and plug outlet loads. It includes oil or gas furnace and any other appliances such as built–in vacuum systems (which are rated 12.5 amps or less), swimming pool pump motors, most workshop motors, compactor motors, garburators, air conditioners, each individually rated at not more than 1500 watts (this is 12.5 amps at 120 volts) but does not include electric heating.

Step 2   <u>**Appliances**</u>

Range (standard size is 12 kw) — add 6000 watts .... = _____ watts

> **Note** — 6000 watts is not a percentage of the range rating — it would be 6000 watts for any size range up to 12 kw.

2nd. Range - add 25% of it's wattage. (25% of 12000 for a 12kw range.)................. = _____ watts

(Appendix for Rule 8-200, page 441 in the code, requires 100%. That is an editorial error, ignore it, 25% is ok.)

Dryer — add 25% of rating .... = _____ watts

Water heater — add 25% of rating .... = _____ watts

Note — If this is all the load we have, i.e. if heating is with gas or oil and there is no other large load such as electric sauna etc. then we must determine **minimum service size** here as follows:

[a]   **If the floor area is less than 80 m^2** — this includes the area of all the floors but does **not** include the basement. The basement floor area is ignored completely for this determination.

     Then — minimum service size must be 60 amps. See Table of Material Sizes, page 5.

[b]   **If the floor area is 80 m^2 or more** — for this determination, as in (a) above, we may ignore completely the basement floor area.

     Then — minimum service size must be 100 amp. See Table of Material Sizes, page 5.

Step 3   <u>**Sauna**</u> — the code now calls this space heating.

Add the sauna load at 100% if the house heating is **not** with electricity .... = _____ watts
If the house **is** electrically heated see under specific type of heating below.

Step 4   <u>**Electric Baseboards & Sauna**</u>

Baseboard heaters .... = _____ watts
Sauna heaters .... = _____ watts
          Total = _____ watts

1st. 10 kw must be added at 100% .... = _____ watts
All the balance may be added at 75% .... = _____ watts

                           Total = _____ watts

     Divide $\dfrac{\text{Total watts}}{240 \text{ volts}}$ = _____ amps

Step 5   <u>**Electric Hot Air Furnace & Sauna**</u>

Add 100% of furnace nameplate rating .... = _____ amps
Add sauna at 75% of it's nameplate rating .... = _____ amps

            Total amps = _____ amps

                  Min. service size is _____ amps

Now consult the lists of materials on page 2.

EXAMPLE 1

An average 120 m² (1291 sq. ft.) house. It has a 60 m² (646 sq. ft.) basement. The electrical load consists of 12 kw. range, 4 kw. dryer, 3 kw. water heater, 3 kw. sauna and 11 kw. electric baseboard heating. Calculate service size.

Basic Load	Floor area = 120 m² main floor at 100%	=	120 m²
	60 m² basement at 75%	=	45 m²
	Total	=	165 m²

First 90 m² .... 5000 watts

next 75 m² .... 1000 watts

range .... 6000 watts

dryer .... 1000 watts

water heater .... 750 watts

electric heating & sauna = 11 kw. plus 3 kw. = 14 kw.

1st. 10 kw. at 100% .... 10000 watts

bal. 4 kw. at 75% .... 3000 watts

Total = 26750 watts

$$\frac{26750}{240} = 111.5 \text{ amps}$$

Now refer to the lists of materials on page 2.

Our load is 111.5 amps. This is greater than list B, which is 100 amps, but less than C, which is 120 amps. Therefore we may use list C.

CAUTION − Don't ignore the note regarding the panel. The panel for list C may not supply baseboard heaters − but that is what this question requires. Therefore, we must use list D because we need a 30 circuit panel for this load.

SUB-FEEDER SIZES to 2nd. PANEL

It is often an advantage to install a second panel near the kitchen load. The sizes of panels and feeders and other details are dealt with on page 31.

2 SERVICE CONDUCTOR TYPES − Rule 12−102, Bulletin 12-3-0

(a) **Copper / Aluminum Conductors**

The service conductor may be either copper or aluminum. Aluminum conductor installation requires great care.

(b) **Service Conductor Insulation**

Mild Coastal Regions − Where the outside temperature does not regularly drop below 10°C. (14°F.) the conductor insulation may be, for example, ... RW, R90, or even TW

This includes all the following areas: all Vancouver Island districts, and
all Lower Mainland districts, and
Chilliwack district, and
Prince Rupert district, and
Powell River and Squamish district, and
The Gulf Islands, University of British Columbia, Howe Sound and Bella Coola districts, and
Terrace district.

In Colder Regions − All areas not included in the above list where the outside temperature regularly drops well below 10°C. the conductor insulation must be approved for this lower temperature. Look for the surface printed marking on the conductors. It will say "Minus 40C" or "(−40C)". You may use conductors such as .. TW−40 or R90 or RW90 or others which have the -40C marking.

3 HYDRO SERVICE WIRES to the HOUSE

(a) Consult Hydro – Rules 6-114(a) & (b), 6-210, Bulletin 6-3-0 & Bulletin 6-2-0

Before any work is done the power utility should be consulted to determine which pole the service will be from. This is very important. The entrance cap must be properly located with respect to the Hydro pole.

There are a number of details to watch out for when locating the service entrance cap:

A **Entrance Cap above Line Insulator** - Rule 6-114 which requires the entrance cap to be located 6 in. above the line insulator has been relaxed. In most cases it will be permissible to locate the entrance cap below the line insulator. However, you may be in a locality where it is not permitted because of the type of splicing device used by your local Hydro crew. Check with your local Inspector.

B **Roof Crossing** - Rule 6-114(c) says the entrance cap must be located so that the service leads need not cross over the roof of **any building** except the roof **overhang** as shown in the illustration.

C **Fire Fighting Operations** - Bulletin 6-3-0 says to keep the overhead lines off the roof and out of the way of fire fighters. Only the roof overhang may be crossed.

D **Heavy Snowfall Areas** - Bulletin 6-2-0 says the three locations shown along the side of the roof in the illustration below may not be acceptable in heavy snowfall areas. Check with your local Inspector.

The illustration below shows some service locations which **are acceptable** and some which are **not acceptable.**

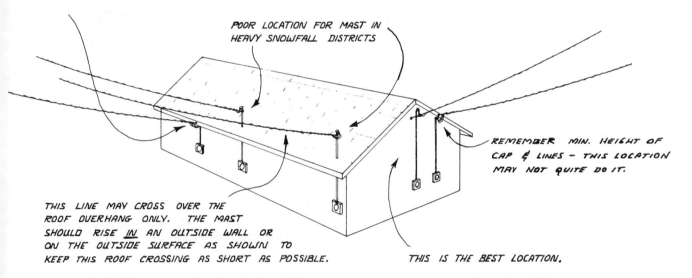

(b) Minimum Line to Ground Clearances – Rule 6-110, Bulletin 12-4-0

The insulator, shown below, required by Hydro for their service drop, must be installed high enough to provide the following minimum clearances:

	Meters	Feet
Public roadways	5.5	18.0
Driveways		
commercial / industrial premises	5.0	16.4
residential premises	4.5	14.76
Sundeck	2.5	8.2
Lawns – pedestrian only areas	3.5	11.5

(d) **Sundeck Crossing** – Rule 12-310, Bulletin 12-4-0

You may cross over the sundeck or balcony with the overhead service lines as shown below.

The clearance above the deck has been reduced to 8.2 ft. (2.5 m). It was 10 ft. in the last code - maybe we'r not as tall as we used to be.

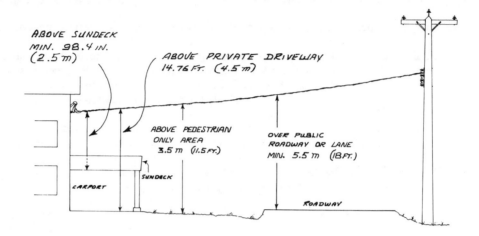

(e) **Hydro Line Attachment to House** – Rules 2-108, 6-110, 6-114(c)

Hydro requires that you provide and install an insulator on the building for their line crew to attach their service cable. This wireholder must:

– be **insulated** type, even for triplex cable.

– be located within 24 in. of the entrance cap.

– be high enough to maintain all the line to ground clearances given above.

– be carefully located so that the 1 m (39.4 in.) line to window and door clearances can be maintained. See page 12.

– be sufficiently well anchored in a structural member of the building to withstand the pull of the lines in a storm.

Note – In the previous code Rule 6-110(6), which requires a bolt, was officially amended by interpretation to allow a lag screw type wireholder as shown by Circ. C 14/83. This amendment is not valid under the new code however the practice of accepting a lag screw type insulator is well established and will no doubt continue. BC Hydro requires the type shown.

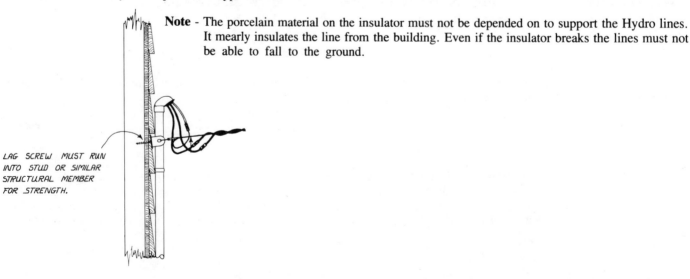

Note - The porcelain material on the insulator must not be depended on to support the Hydro lines. It mearly insulates the line from the building. Even if the insulator breaks the lines must not be able to fall to the ground.

4. SERVICE ENTRANCE CAP - for **overhead** services only.

(a) Consult Hydro — Rules 6-110, 6-114(a) & 6-210

Before begining the installation of your electrical service, be sure to obtain from the supply authority (BC Hydro or the equivalent in your area) the correct location of the pole from which you will receive service. Your service head must be properly located with respect to the Hydro service pole.

(b) Type of Cap to Use — Rule 6-112

Slip-on Type

(c) Height of Entrance Cap

There are two things to watch for:

1st. — that you can obtain the minimum line to ground clearances, given on page 9,

AND

2nd. — wherever possible Rule 6-114(b) says the entrance cap should be (the revised Rule does **not** say it must be) **higher** than the wireholder which supports the Hydro line. This Rule now says the cap should be, not must be, between 150 mm and 300 mm (between 6 to 12 in.) **above** the Hydro line insulator as shown in the sketch above and on page 9.

If, in your case, it is dificult to locate the cap **above the line insulator** it's probably ok below the insulator but you should check with your local Inspector first.

Some background information for the student.

Rule 6-114b was originally designed to prevent water travelling down the Hydro service line to the splices at the entrance cap and there, at the splice, find its way into the conductor itself. Water in this location would be drawn along by capillary action between the conductor strands and on down to the meter base where it would collect and do all kinds of nasty things.

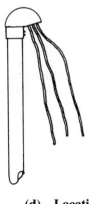

In the new code this rule was modified to take into account the special splicing sleeve used by BC Hydro line crews. This sleeve has a gasket at each end and a **total barrier** in the middle to prevent water entry and migration across the splice. To my knowledge this splicing sleeve is used for line connections in all areas served by BC Hydro.

Rule 6-302(3) requires that you leave at least 750 mm (29.5 in.) of service conductor hanging out of the entrance cap.

This long length may seem wasteful and sometimes is, but that's what the rule requires. The purpose is to provide sufficient length for Hydro crews to form acceptable drip loops that will prevent water following the service conductors into the service conduit and down into the service equipment.

(d) Location of Entrance Cap — Rule 6-110, Bulletin 6-1-0

This is an "out of reach" rule. The entrance cap must be placed so that **all** open conductors are above the window. If they are below or alongside the window, or if they run in front of the window, as shown below, they must be at least 1 m(39.37 in.) away from the window. This rule applies to all windows even those which cannot be opened.

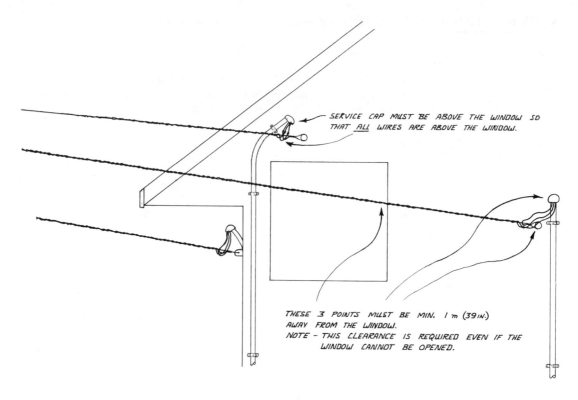

SERVICE CAP MUST BE ABOVE THE WINDOW SO
THAT ALL WIRES ARE ABOVE THE WINDOW.

THESE 3 POINTS MUST BE MIN. 1 m (39 IN.)
AWAY FROM THE WINDOW.
NOTE - THIS CLEARANCE IS REQUIRED EVEN IF THE
WINDOW CANNOT BE OPENED.

Note — A long drip loop is **not** approved. Locate the entrance cap within 24 in. of the point of attachment of the service drop wires. Service drop leads may contact the building at **one** point only. They may not run along the building through two or more insulators to get to the cap location except by **special permission**. See amended rule 6-302(2).

NOTE — Snow Slides - Bulletin 6-2-0 (1)(e)

Many services have been pulled out or have been severely damaged by snow sliding off a roof during the winter

months. It is important that the entrance cap be very carefully located so that such slides cannot harm the service conduit and the Hydro service lines. The gable end of the roof is the preferred location for the entrance cap.

In the illustration above, one example shows the service leads terminating on the wall below the roof overhang. This is a poor location because snow sliding off the roof during the winter months could damage these lines — actually pull them out.

Note — Service masts which run through any part of a roof, particularly the lower part of a roof, **may** also not be acceptable to some utility companies, therefore, in heavy snowfall districts the entrance cap should be located on the **gable end** or similar location on the house where it will not be subject to damage by snow slides.

5. SERVICE MAST REQUIREMENTS — Rule 6-110, Bulletin 6-2-0

Where a service mast is needed to raise the entrance cap and service leads to the required height, the following should be complied with:

WOOD MAST — Note dimensions

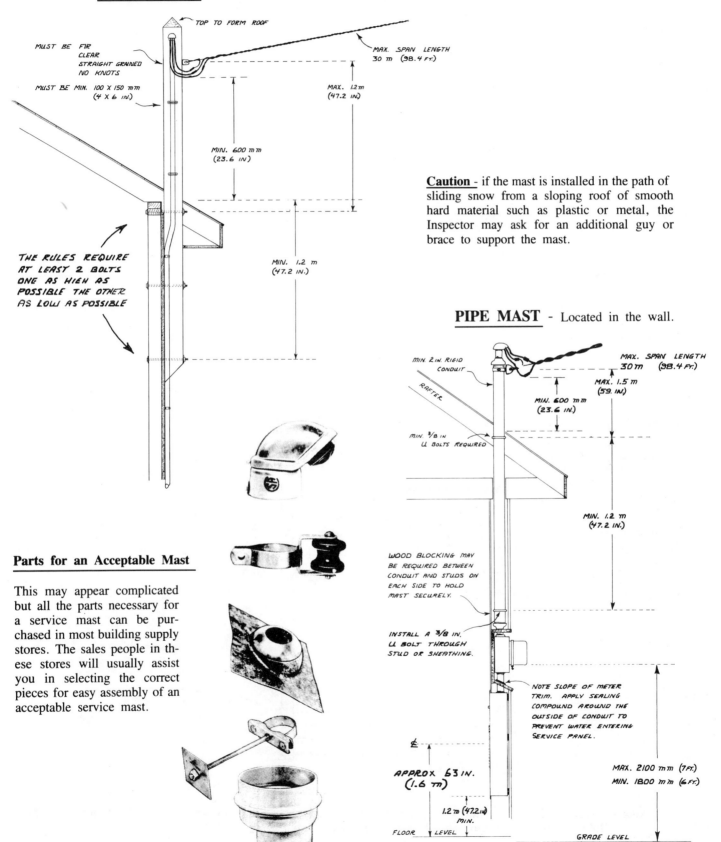

Caution - if the mast is installed in the path of sliding snow from a sloping roof of smooth hard material such as plastic or metal, the Inspector may ask for an additional guy or brace to support the mast.

PIPE MAST - Located in the wall.

Parts for an Acceptable Mast

This may appear complicated but all the parts necessary for a service mast can be purchased in most building supply stores. The sales people in these stores will usually assist you in selecting the correct pieces for easy assembly of an acceptable service mast.

PIPE MAST - Surface mounted

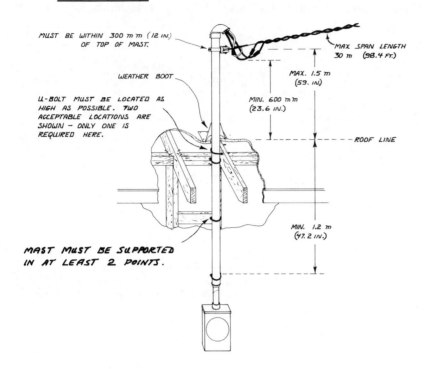

MUST BE WITHIN 300 mm (12 IN.) OF TOP OF MAST.

WEATHER BOOT

U-BOLT MUST BE LOCATED AS HIGH AS POSSIBLE. TWO ACCEPTABLE LOCATIONS ARE SHOWN - ONLY ONE IS REQUIRED HERE.

MAST MUST BE SUPPORTED IN AT LEAST 2 POINTS.

MAX SPAN LENGTH 30 m (98.4 FT.)

MAX. 1.5 m (59. IN.)

MIN. 600 mm (23.6 IN.)

ROOF LINE

MIN. 1.2 m (47.2 IN.)

MAST for FLAT ROOF - Rule 12-310

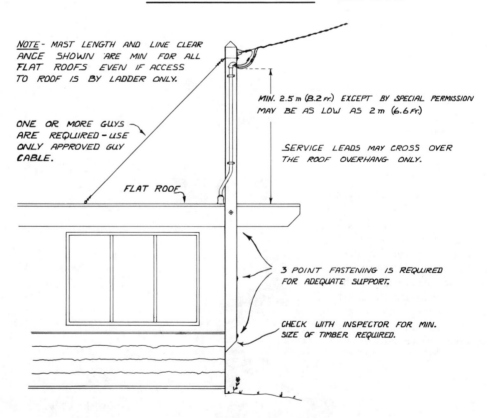

NOTE - MAST LENGTH AND LINE CLEARANCE SHOWN ARE MIN FOR ALL FLAT ROOFS EVEN IF ACCESS TO ROOF IS BY LADDER ONLY.

ONE OR MORE GUYS ARE REQUIRED - USE ONLY APPROVED GUY CABLE.

FLAT ROOF

MIN. 2.5 m (8.2 FT.) EXCEPT BY SPECIAL PERMISSION MAY BE AS LOW AS 2 m (6.6 FT.)

SERVICE LEADS MAY CROSS OVER THE ROOF OVERHANG ONLY.

3 POINT FASTENING IS REQUIRED FOR ADEQUATE SUPPORT.

CHECK WITH INSPECTOR FOR MIN. SIZE OF TIMBER REQUIRED.

Note - If this roof is also a **sundeck** the minimum line clearance above the roof would also be 98.4 inches (2.5 m) Bulletin 12-4-0. See also under Sundecks on page 11.

6 LENGTH OF SERVICE CONDUCTOR — Rule 6-210(1)(d), 6-212 & Bulletin 6-4-0

According to the rule the service panel must be located " as close as practicable to the point where the service conductors enter the building." That's a good rule — keep it as short as possible for two good reasons.

(1) because it is an unprotected conductor — only the Hydro line fuse, which is ahead of the transformer, is protecting you, and

(2) the service run is very costly.

Maximum length permitted (without special permission) is ....6 m (20 ft.)

Note: In the wall, in the attic, or in the crawl space is considered in the building.

For example —If your service is 8 m (26.3 ft.) long you would need to:

(a) run at least 2 m(6.5 ft.) of this length on the outside **surface** of the building (if it is inside a wall it is considered inside the building) or,

(b) run at least 2 m(6.5 ft.) buried under the floor, **actually buried**, not just in the crawl space.

    Note — EMT may not be directly buried. For **underground** runs use rigid metal or PVC conduit.

(c) run at least 2 m(6.5 ft.) encased in not less than 50 mm (2 in.) of concrete. This section could be laid in the concrete floor or if too late for that, it could be laid on top of the **concrete floor** and a 50 mm (2 in.) minimum layer of concrete poured over it as shown. Rule 6-212(a).

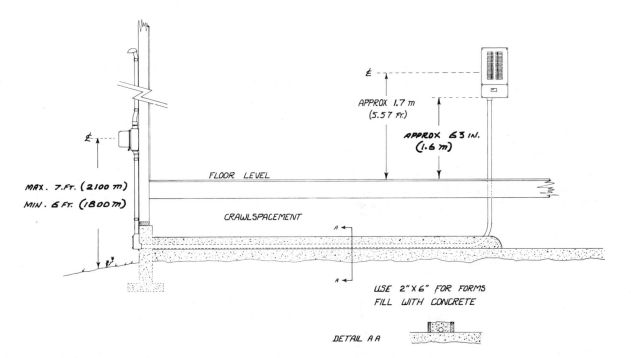

7 SERVICE CONDUIT or SERVICE CABLE

There are several different wiring methods permitted for service conductors.

(a) **EMT — Thinwall Conduit** — Rule 6-302(1)(c)

This is a thinwall conduit which **cannot be threaded**. It requires very few tools for installation.

(i) **Length** — The maximum permitted inside the building is 6 m (20 ft.) — see page 16.

(ii) **Couplings & Connectors** — Rule 12-1510

Set Screw Type and Compression Type

There are two main types of thinwall conduit couplings used today.

Compression
Coupling

Set Screw
Coupling

Compression
Connector

Set Screw
Connector

Set Screw Type

These may be used indoors or directly under a roof overhang or in concrete **but may not** be exposed to the weather.

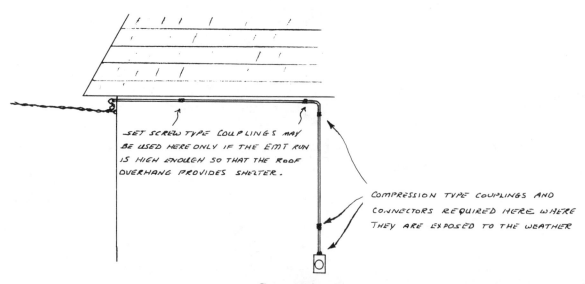

SET SCREW TYPE COUPLINGS MAY BE USED HERE ONLY IF THE EMT RUN IS HIGH ENOUGH SO THAT THE ROOF OVERHANG PROVIDES SHELTER.

COMPRESSION TYPE COUPLINGS AND CONNECTORS REQUIRED HERE WHERE THEY ARE EXPOSED TO THE WEATHER

Compression Type may be used in all cases wherever EMT is permitted.

(iii) **Fittings, L.B.'s, etc.**

Ahead of Meter

L.B. FITTING

Power companies do not allow conduit fittings to be installed ahead of the meter base, however, on the load side of the base you may install as many as you require. Where it cannot be avoided and a fitting must be installed ahead of the base, you should seek Hydro permission first before proceeding.

AVOID THESE CONDUIT FITTINGS IF AT ALL POSSIBLE EVEN ON THE LOAD SIDE OF THE METER BECAUSE IT CAN BE VERY DIFFICULT TO GET THE CONDUCTORS TO LIE PROPERLY IN THE FITTING. THE CONDUCTORS FOR 100 AMP. AND LARGER SERVICES ARE VERY STIFF.

NEVER USE TWO FITTINGS BACK TO BACK AS SHOWN WHEN THE SERVICE CONDUCTORS ARE #2 OR LARGER.

IT IS TOO DIFFICULT TO FORCE THESE CONDUCTORS INTO THIS 2ND. FITTING. REPLACE THIS FITTING WITH A 90° CONDUIT BEND.

Accessible

Don't try to hide that LB fitting in the wall because the Inspector is on the look-out for that sort of thing. Fittings must remain accessible. These may be in the meter opening as shown in Fig. A.

Fig. A.   Fig. B.

The square meter base eliminates the need for most of the fittings below the base, as shown in Fig. B.

(iv) **Bends** – Rule 12-1514

The maximum permitted is the equivalent of four quarter bends (4 – 90° bends). These must be made without damage to the pipe.

(v) **Locknut and Bushings** – Rule 10-604 & Bulletin 12-8-0

Locknuts – Rule 10-602 – To provide adequate bonding, two locknuts and one bushing is required for rigid conduit. Fig. A below.

Note – locknuts are dished, that is they are not flat. They are designed to bite through the paint or rust and into the metal of the box. This is necessary to provide good grounding for the equipment.

Bushings – Rule 12-1006 – Where the conductors are **larger** than #8, the bushings must be insulated type such as plastic, or have an insulating ring, such as plastic, mounted in the bushing to protect the conductors.

EMT (Thinwall conduit) REQUIRES a LOCKNUT **AND** BUSHING.

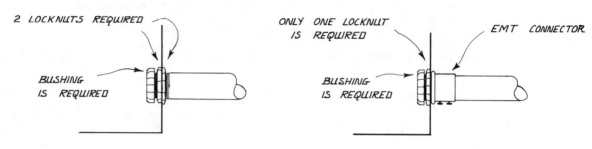

FIG A. RIGID CONDUIT   FIG B. THINWALL CONDUIT

(vi)   **Strapping** – Rules 12-1112 & 12-1504

Install one strap near the top end, another near the meter base. Install additional straps as required to keep the distance between straps to a maximum 2 m (approx. 6 ft.).

(vii)   **Sealing** – Rules 6-312   &   Bulletin 6-8-0(1)

The seal required by this rule prevents the warmer inside air from escaping through the service conduit. It has been found that the warm air, if allowed to flow, condenses to water in sufficient quantity to damage the service equipment. While this seal was formerly required only in the very cold regions, it is now thought necessary to require it in every electrical service anywhere in B.C. You should check with your Inspector.

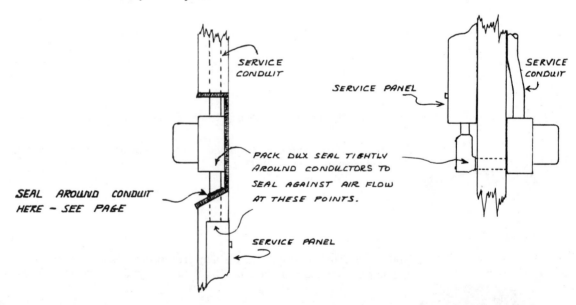

This seal is usually made with a soft putty-like substance called DUX SEAL. To be most effective the DUX SEAL is placed around the conductors in the last opening, before the conduit leaves the warmer area.

(b) **P.V.C. Conduit** – Rule 6-302(a). Bulletin 6-7-0(1)&(2)

This conduit has some real advantages – very few tools are required to install it.

— Be sure to remove rough burrs from the inside edge of the pipe ends, where it has been cut. Do this with any knife.

— Be sure the pipe and fitting is clean and dry before applying solvent cement.

P.V.C. ENTRANCE CAP

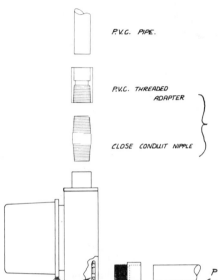

P.V.C. PIPE.

P.V.C. THREADED ADAPTER

CLOSE CONDUIT NIPPLE

THIS ARRANGEMENT MUST BE USED HERE RULE 12-1210. THE THREADED MALE ADAPTER SHOWN BELOW MAY NOT BE USED HERE

METAL LOCKNUT   PVC ADAPTER

PVC CONDUIT TO PANEL. (RIGID METAL CONDUIT COULD BE USED HERE INSTEAD.)

Note – PVC may be used between the meter base and the service panel, as shown, but for short runs it is not recommended.

PVC pipe may not be enclosed or covered in building insulation, rule 12-1202(d) and Bulletin 6-7-0(2), except for very short lengths, not exceeding 6 inches. The illustration shows an example of PVC pipe running through an insulated wall to the panel.

It is simpler to use a rigid metal conduit nipple with 2 locknuts and a plastic bushing at each end.

Meter Base Bonding – be sure to connect the neutral conductor to the meter base. See under meter connections, page 27.

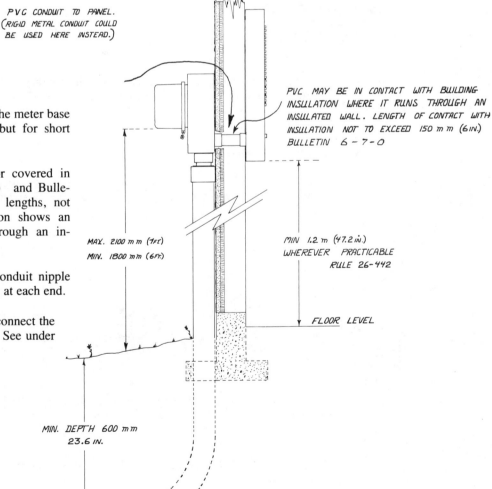

PVC MAY BE IN CONTACT WITH BUILDING INSULATION WHERE IT RUNS THROUGH AN INSULATED WALL. LENGTH OF CONTACT WITH INSULATION NOT TO EXCEED 150 mm (6 IN.) BULLETIN 6 - 7 - 0

MAX. 2100 mm (7 FT.)
MIN. 1800 mm (6 FT.)

MIN. 1.2 m (47.2 IN.) WHEREVER PRACTICABLE RULE 26-442

FLOOR LEVEL

MIN. DEPTH 600 mm 23.6 IN.

(c) **Service Cable**

    (i)   **Type**

        Rule 6-302. Type teck90 cable is permitted for service work. It is easier to install than conduit.

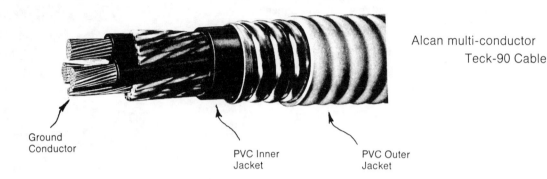

Alcan multi-conductor
Teck-90 Cable

Ground
Conductor

PVC Inner
Jacket

PVC Outer
Jacket

    (ii)   **Size**

        The ampacity of cable is the same as an equivalent size conductor in conduit. See pages 2 & 3 for sizes required.

    (iii)   **Type of Entrance Cap to Use** – Rule 6-112

Heat Shrink – a kind of plastic sock that slips over the top end of your service cable. Trim the cable as required – you should have three insulated conductors sticking out of the armour, as shown.

Slip this sock in place, then heat it with an open gas torch or heat gun or even heat lamps will do, as long as the heat applied is approximately 250°F. The sock will shrink to fit snugly in place. It will seal it from rain but remember, it must still **face downwards** when installed. Allow enough length to do this.

    (iv)   **Cable Connectors**

Use weatherproof connectors where cable connects to the top of the meter base. Be sure to use the correct size and type for the cable you are using. Your supplier will advise you on this.

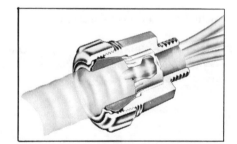

Dry type connectors may be used where it is not exposed to the weather – as shown in the illustration.

(v)   **Length Permitted** -   Bulletin 6-4-0(2)

Maximum 20 ft. (6 m) inside the house. Remember, this length is measured from the point where the cable enters the house to the service box. See page 16 for more information.

(vi)   **Strapping** -   Rule 12-718

Cable must be strapped within 12 in. of the connector at each end and every 60 inches (1.5 m).

(vii)   **Meter Connections** -   Rules 10-518(2) & 10-906(3)

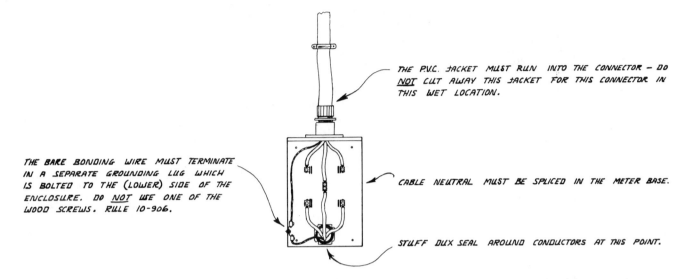

THE P.V.C. JACKET MUST RUN INTO THE CONNECTOR – DO NOT CUT AWAY THIS JACKET FOR THIS CONNECTOR IN THIS WET LOCATION.

THE BARE BONDING WIRE MUST TERMINATE IN A SEPARATE GROUNDING LUG WHICH IS BOLTED TO THE (LOWER) SIDE OF THE ENCLOSURE. DO NOT USE ONE OF THE WOOD SCREWS. RULE 10-906.

CABLE NEUTRAL MUST BE SPLICED IN THE METER BASE.

STUFF DUX SEAL AROUND CONDUCTORS AT THIS POINT.

(viii) **Mechanical Damage** – Greater care is needed when installing this cable than is required when installing EMT conduit. This cable is more easily damaged with driven nails or where it is run on the surface of a wall.

In the illustration below, the cable is shown running through the plate and over the broken edge of the foundation wall. This section of cable is subject to damage and must be protected. Use heavy gauge metal plates to protect the cable at these points. The side plates of metal outlet boxes do this very well.

Where the cable is run on the surface of the wall and where it may be subject to mechanical damage (in locations such as a garage or carport for example) the cable may be protected with wooden or metal guards or a short section of metal pipe may be used.

The illustration below shows teck cable being used above the meter base to an overhead supply and from the meter base to the panel. It also shows PVC conduit from the meter base downwards to an underground Hydro system, where this is required. Obviously, only one of these systems will be available — either overhead supply or underground supply and therefore only the teck cable running up or the PVC conduit running down is necessary.

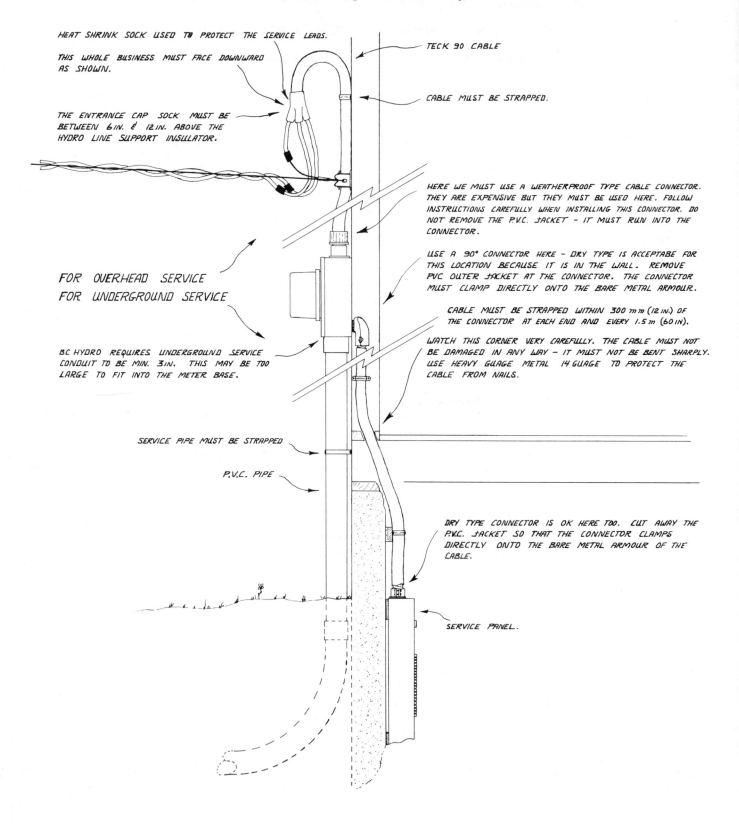

HEAT SHRINK SOCK USED TO PROTECT THE SERVICE LEADS.

THIS WHOLE BUSINESS MUST FACE DOWNWARD AS SHOWN.

THE ENTRANCE CAP SOCK MUST BE BETWEEN 6 IN. & 12 IN. ABOVE THE HYDRO LINE SUPPORT INSULATOR.

TECK 90 CABLE

CABLE MUST BE STRAPPED.

HERE WE MUST USE A WEATHERPROOF TYPE CABLE CONNECTOR. THEY ARE EXPENSIVE BUT THEY MUST BE USED HERE. FOLLOW INSTRUCTIONS CAREFULLY WHEN INSTALLING THIS CONNECTOR. DO NOT REMOVE THE P.V.C. JACKET — IT MUST RUN INTO THE CONNECTOR.

USE A 90° CONNECTOR HERE — DRY TYPE IS ACCEPTABE FOR THIS LOCATION BECAUSE IT IS IN THE WALL. REMOVE PVC OUTER JACKET AT THE CONNECTOR. THE CONNECTOR MUST CLAMP DIRECTLY ONTO THE BARE METAL ARMOUR.

CABLE MUST BE STRAPPED WITHIN 300 mm (12 IN.) OF THE CONNECTOR AT EACH END AND EVERY 1.5 m (60 IN).

WATCH THIS CORNER VERY CAREFULLY. THE CABLE MUST NOT BE DAMAGED IN ANY WAY — IT MUST NOT BE BENT SHARPLY. USE HEAVY GUAGE METAL 14 GUAGE TO PROTECT THE CABLE FROM NAILS.

FOR OVERHEAD SERVICE
FOR UNDERGROUND SERVICE

BC HYDRO REQUIRES UNDERGROUND SERVICE CONDUIT TO BE MIN. 3 IN. THIS MAY BE TOO LARGE TO FIT INTO THE METER BASE.

SERVICE PIPE MUST BE STRAPPED

P.V.C. PIPE

DRY TYPE CONNECTOR IS OK HERE TOO. CUT AWAY THE P.V.C. JACKET SO THAT THE CONNECTOR CLAMPS DIRECTLY ONTO THE BARE METAL ARMOUR OF THE CABLE.

SERVICE PANEL.

8. UNDERGROUND SERVICE CONDUIT – from underground supply.

Re: B.C. Hydro Eng. Standard for underground ducting.

(a) Trench

It is the owners or contractors responsibility to prepare the needed trench for the service duct.

(i) Depth – 900 mm(35.4 in.)

(ii) Length – From Hydro service box to the house.

(iii) Pull–in Cord

Don't forget to install a pull cord in the pipe for the Hydro installation crew – This is a must. They will use this cord to draw in a heavy rope to pull in the service cables.

(iv) Sand Bed

In very rocky earth the Hydro may require a layer of sand both below and above the pipe to protect it.

Note – Do not backfill trench until approved by Hydro Inspector.

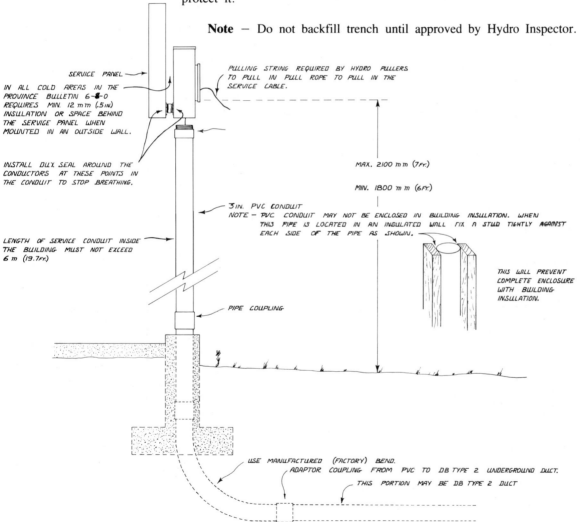

SERVICE PANEL

IN ALL COLD AREAS IN THE PROVINCE BULLETIN 6-8-0 REQUIRES MIN. 12 mm (.5 IN) INSULATION OR SPACE BEHIND THE SERVICE PANEL WHEN MOUNTED IN AN OUTSIDE WALL.

INSTALL DUX SEAL AROUND THE CONDUCTORS AT THESE POINTS IN THE CONDUIT TO STOP BREATHING.

LENGTH OF SERVICE CONDUIT INSIDE THE BUILDING MUST NOT EXCEED 6 m (19.7 FT.)

PULLING STRING REQUIRED BY HYDRO PULLERS TO PULL IN PULL ROPE TO PULL IN THE SERVICE CABLE.

MAX. 2100 mm (7 FT.)

MIN. 1800 mm (6 FT.)

3 IN. PVC CONDUIT
NOTE – PVC CONDUIT MAY NOT BE ENCLOSED IN BUILDING INSULATION. WHEN THIS PIPE IS LOCATED IN AN INSULATED WALL FIX A STUD TIGHTLY AGAINST EACH SIDE OF THE PIPE AS SHOWN.

THIS WILL PREVENT COMPLETE ENCLOSURE WITH BUILDING INSULATION.

PIPE COUPLING

USE MANUFACTURED (FACTORY) BEND.
ADAPTOR COUPLING FROM PVC TO DB TYPE 2 UNDERGROUND DUCT.
THIS PORTION MAY BE DB TYPE 2 DUCT

(b) Duct

Hydro requires this duct to run all the way to their connection point at the property line. Contact Hydro for location of trench termination at the property line.

(i) Type

Use DB type 2 pipe – available at most building supply stores. (Don't try to use that white B.C. telephone duct – not good enough).

(ii) **Size**

Minimum 3 in. diameter for all services up to and including 200 amp.

(iii) **Bends**

Must have 90 degree bend below meter base at the house, as shown. Hydro will allow only one additional 45 degree bend in this run. Avoid this additional bend if you can but if you need it, use it. It may be anywhere between the meter base and the Hydro connection point at the property line.

(iv) **200 Amp Meter Base Required**

Hydro wants a 200 amp meter base even if you are installing only a 100 amp service. The reason for this is twofold: First, they need the larger base to provide adequate space when installing their large service cables. Secondly, they insist on a very large underground service conduit. The minimum size they will accept is 3 in. conduit even for the 100 amp service. Because the 100 amp meter base does not have a large enough KO hole to receive the 3 in. service conduit they want us to use 200 amp meter bases. Make sure your base is punched for 3 in. conduit.

(c) **Sealing** — Rule 6-312, Bulletin 6-8-0

The seal required by this rule prevents the warmer inside air from escaping through the service conduit. It has been found that the warm air, if allowed to flow, condenses to water in sufficient quantity to damage the service equipment. While this seal was formerly required only in the very cold regions, it is now thought necessary to require it in every electrical service anywhere in B.C. You should check with your local Inspector.

This seal is usually made with a soft, putty—like substance called DUX SEAL. To be most effective the DUX SEAL is placed around the conductors in the last opening before the conduit leaves the warmer area. See illustration of two typical services.

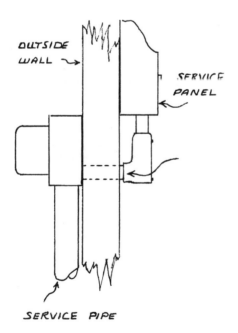

OUTSIDE WALL

SERVICE PANEL

SERVICE PIPE

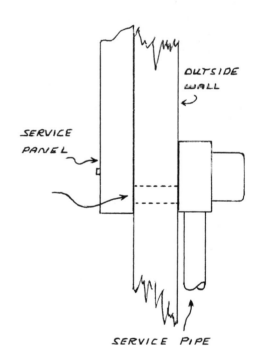

OUTSIDE WALL

SERVICE PANEL

SERVICE PIPE

9. **METER BASE INSTALLATION** – Bulletin 6-9-0

(a) **Types**

In general there are two types of meter bases available, the round and the square. Either one is acceptable. Make sure your base has the correct rating in amperes.

Note 1 **For an underground service** use a 200 amp. meter base. This large base must be used to provide adequate working space for Hydro crew to do their work inside the base. One more thing, make sure there is a 3 in. KO hole in the bottom of the base for the 3 in. service conduit required by Hydro.

Note 2 **If the knockouts** provided by the manufacturer of the base are not in the correct position and new holes need to be punched out, these new holes **must be totally below any live parts in the meter base**. Only where a meter base is installed **totally indoors**, as in a service room, may new holes may be cut above the live parts in the base.

By the way, if you plan to use an old **round** type meter base which has side or back conduit entry holes, be careful. Back entry into round meter bases is not approved. The side entry on these round bases may only be used for small conductors - up to #6 is ok but nothing larger. Better to use only the top and bottom entries and close off the others.

(b) **Locations** – Hydro Metering Guide

Meter locations must be carefully chosen. Some of the things to watch for are:

(i) **Carports**

If you plan to face your meter base into the carport you should know that there is no code rule or bulletin which specifically says you may not have it there. However, before you install it in the carport you should talk to your local Hydro people. They may not like it there.

Fact is, no matter how careful you are as a driver, when you are backing in your 24 ft. Winnebago that meter is subject to damage when it faces into the carport.

Every year there are thousands of carports closed in to make a garage or an additional bedroom. If the meter faces into the carport the cost of the simple closing in of a carport can become too costly because it would involve a service change.

(ii) **Porch**

If it is an open porch it may be an acceptable location now but remember you may want to close it in later on in the future. A closed in porch is a heat saver in the winter time, so avoid the hassle, follow old Chinese proverb – don't do it in the porch.

(c) **Height** – Rule 6–408 and Hydro Metering Guide

Meters shall be located on an outside wall, facing out, not higher than 2100 mm(82.7 in.) and not less than 1800 mm(70.9 in.) above grade, except that they may be located between 2100 mm(82.7 in.) and 1200 mm(47.2 in.) above grade level if fully recessed into wall openings. All heights to be measured from the bottom of the base to permanent ground level. One more thing, the minimum height may be reduced to 1200 mm(47.2 in.) for meters mounted on the surface of the house if the meter is protected by a projection not more than 600 mm(23.6 in.) from the meter, such as a chimney or inside corner.

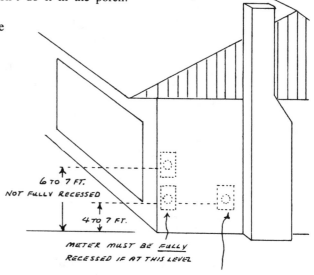

6 TO 7 FT.
NOT FULLY RECESSED

4 TO 7 FT.

METER MUST BE FULLY RECESSED IF AT THIS LEVEL

MAY BE ON SURFACE OR PARTIALLY RECESSED. THIS METER IS PROTECTED BY THE CHIMNEY

(d) Connections

Rule 10−518(2) requires the neutral to be connected to the meter base as shown. Simply bare a section of the neutral conductor where it passes the bonding terminal in the meter base − then slip it into the lug provided and tighten. Do not cut this conductor.

INCOMING BLACK WIRES CONNECT TO TOP TWO TERMINALS.
LOAD BLACK WIRES CONNECT TO LOWER TERMINALS.

WHITE WIRE IS ALSO USED TO GROUND THE METER BASE
−RULE 10-518(2) − CONNECT IT TO THE GROUNDING
TERMINAL IN THE BASE. DO NOT CUT THIS CONDUCTOR
−SIMPLY BARE A SECTION AND LAY IN CONNECTOR.

240 VOLTS 3 WIRE

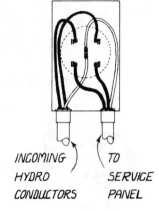

INCOMING
HYDRO
CONDUCTORS

TO
SERVICE
PANEL

(e) Support

Support the meter base with wood screws through the two or more factory drilled holes in the back of the base. Make sure it is in a reasonably accurate upright position.

(f) Blank Cover − Bulletin 6−9−0

A disk of ¼ in. plywood may be used. In some districts the power utility will energize the electrical service but will not install a meter until several days later. During this time a blank cover is required to prevent anyone coming in contact with live parts.

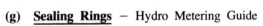

(g) Sealing Rings − Hydro Metering Guide

Sockets must be fitted with screw type sealing rings. The spring clip type are not acceptable.

(h) Fittings, L.B.'s etc.

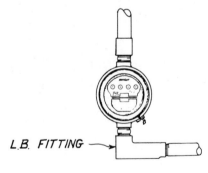

Ahead of Meter − Some power companies do not allow fittings to be installed ahead of a meter base. However, on the load side of the base you may install as many as you require. Where it cannot be avoided and a fitting must be installed ahead of the base, you should seek Hydro permission before proceeding. See also the note on page 18 re: two LB fittings.

L.B. FITTING

10. SERVICE PANEL

(a) Type — Fuse or Breaker Panel

Both are acceptable, however, only the circuit breaker panel is in common use today. For this reason we will deal with circuit breaker panels only.

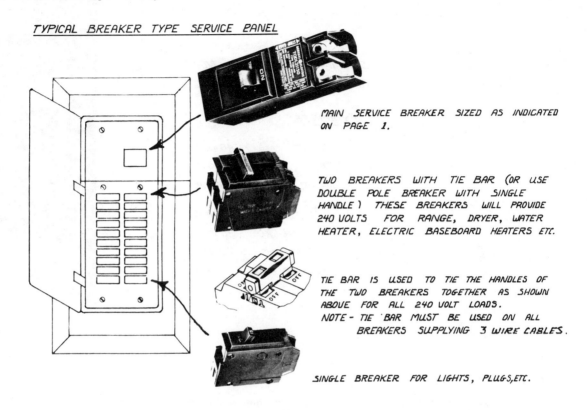

TYPICAL BREAKER TYPE SERVICE PANEL

MAIN SERVICE BREAKER SIZED AS INDICATED ON PAGE 1.

TWO BREAKERS WITH TIE BAR (OR USE DOUBLE POLE BREAKER WITH SINGLE HANDLE) THESE BREAKERS WILL PROVIDE 240 VOLTS FOR RANGE, DRYER, WATER HEATER, ELECTRIC BASEBOARD HEATERS ETC.

TIE BAR IS USED TO TIE THE HANDLES OF THE TWO BREAKERS TOGETHER AS SHOWN ABOVE FOR ALL 240 VOLT LOADS.
NOTE - TIE BAR MUST BE USED ON ALL BREAKERS SUPPLYING 3 WIRE CABLES.

SINGLE BREAKER FOR LIGHTS, PLUGS, ETC.

NOTES - Rule 14-010

3 Wire Cables Entering the Service Panel — The thinking is that someone working on one of the circuit conductors in an outlet box supplied with a 3—wire cable may come in contact with hot conductors on the other circuit unless both circuits are always de—energized together. To eliminate this possible hazard rule 14—010 has been revised to require a tie—bar on circuit breakers. This applies to all 3—wire cables including those supplying light and plug outlets.

Bathroom Razor Outlet — Rule 26-702(9) - These must be supplied with a 'ground fault interrupter' type circuit breaker or you may use a ground fault interrupter type receptacle. The special transformer type razor outlet is no longer approved and may not be installed in new constuction but may only be installed to replace a fauly unit in an existing installation.

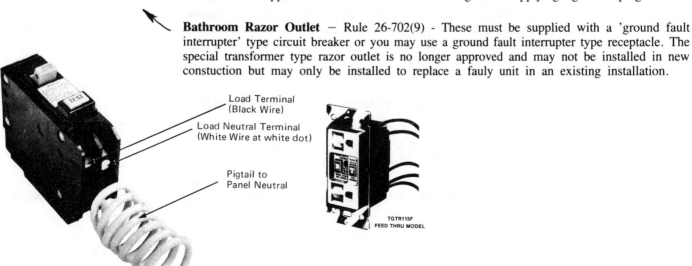

Load Terminal
(Black Wire)

Load Neutral Terminal
(White Wire at white dot)

Pigtail to
Panel Neutral

TGTR115F
FEED THRU MODEL

(b) **Identify Circuits** − **Loads Used** − Rule 2−100(2)&(3)

Use a felt pen or some other permanent manner of marking next to the circuit breaker or fill in the circuit directory card provided by the panel manufacturer. The identification should look something like this.

IDENTIFY LOADS HERE NEXT
TO THE FUSE OR BREAKER.

EXAMPLES

RANGE	*− 40 AMPS.*
DRYER	*− 30 AMPS.*
WATER HEATER	*− 20 AMPS.*
ELECT HEATERS BASEMENT	*−15 AMPS.*
LR & KIT	*− 20 AMPS.*
BEDROOMS	*− 20 AMPS.*
COUNTER PLUG	*−15 AMPS.*

Caution − 2nd Suite

Rule 26-704(1) says that if you are developing a suite in the basement, or eleswhere in the house, you will require a **separate panel for each suite**. The rule requires the panel to be **in the suite** served by the panel. Watch this one, if you miss it in the rough wiring phase it could be a costly mistake.

(c) **How Many Circuits Do I Need?**

The number of circuits needed for a given house is determined by the minimum **SERVICE AMPACITY** as shown on page 5 −−−−−**AND** −−−−−the number of outlets installed in that house.

The table on page 5 has been designed to simplify this problem. This table specifies the required ampere rating of the service and indicates which list of materials should be used for that particular house. Each list of materials indicates the size of panel required.

There are two steps involved − proceed as follows:

Step 1 **Determine minimum number of circuits required from the table on page 5.**

Note − The table on page 5 gives the minimum service ampere rating required. Next to it is a letter in brackets. This letter refers to a list of service material required. This list also indicates the **minimum** number of circuits required for that house.

Step 2 Complete the chart on page 30 to determine the **actual** number of circuits needed to supply the **outlets** you plan to install. Carefully fill in the chart to make sure you do not run short of circuits when the loads are finally being connected.

Result The size of the branch circuit panel must be equal to step 1 or step 2, whichever is **greater**.

Step 3 <u>**MINIMUM CIRCUITS REQUIRED**</u> - Before doing this, read page 43.

Light Outlets .... count all light outlets, indoor and outdoor, (do not
count switch outlets) .... _____

Convenience Plug Outlets

    Living room   Locate plug outlets so that no point along the floor
    Family room   line of the wall is more than 6 ft. (1800 mm) from a
    Bedrooms   plug outlet See page 56 .... _____
    Dining room

Bathroom .... minimum 1 plug receptacle required .... _____

                      Bathroom fan .... _____

Washroom .... Minimum 1 plug receptacle required .... _____

Hallway .... Minimum 1 plug receptacle required for each
                      hallway. See page 57 .... _____

Kitchen fan .... May be supplied with a light circuit .... _____

              TOTAL OUTLETS REQUIRED = _____

then $\dfrac{\text{Total } \textbf{outlets} \text{ required}}{12}$ = **circuits** required .... _____

<u>**ADDITIONAL CIRCUITS REQUIRED**</u>

    Outdoor plug outlets .... Minimum 1 circuit required, See page 66 .... _____

    Carport or Garage .... Minimum 1 circuit required, See page 68 .... _____

    Laundry room or area .... Minimum 1 circuit required, See page 64 .... _____

    Kitchen .... Minimum 1 circuit for fridge .... _____
                      Plus counter outlets, See page 62 .... _____

    Larger Appliances .... Range - 2 circuits required .... _____
                      2 nd. Range - 2 circuits required .... _____
                      Dryer - 2 circuits required .... _____
                      Dishwasher - 1 circuit required .... _____
                      Garburator - 1 circuit required .... _____
                      Compactor - 1 circuit required .... _____
                      Micro-wave oven - 1 circuit required .... _____
                      Instant Hot Water Heater - 1 circuit required .... _____
                      Hydromassage Bath-tub - 1 GFCI circuit required .... _____
                      Built-in Vacuum Cleaner - 1 circuit required .... _____
                      Furnace (gas or oil) - 1 circuit required .... _____
                      Boiler - 1 circuit required .... _____
                      Domestic Use Water Heater - 2 circuits required .... _____
                      Swimming pool - motor load, 1 circuit required .... _____
                                 - lighting load - 1 circuit required .... _____
                      Freezer plug - may be on lighting circuit but better on it's own circuit .... _____
                      Sauna Heater - 2 circuits required .... _____
                      Hot tub - motor load, 1 circuit required .... _____
                                 - electric heater, 2 circuits required .... _____
                      Domestic Water Pump - 1 circuit required (check pump rating) .... _____
                      Plus 2 spare circuits (rule 8-108(2)) .... _____

              TOTAL CIRCUITS REQUIRED = _____

(d) Sub-panel or 2 nd panel

Sometimes it is an advantage to install a 2nd panel to supply the electrical loads in specific areas such as a kitchen or a garage. The kitchen requires a number of separate circuits for special loads such as the fridge, micro-wave oven, compactor etc.. The basement area directly below the kitchen is usually a good location for that second panel. Remenber, the code does not require a 2 nd panel. All the loads in the house may be served from the main service panel. To do this may require a large service panel and a lot of coslty long home runs. For this reason it may be an advantage to install a second panel - it may be a saving.

Don't forget, this second panel must be located with the same care and attention you used to locate the main service panel. All the rules regarding panel location, height, accessibility etc. as outlined below for a main service panel, must also be applied to the second panel. It may not be put just anywhere.

SERVICE PANEL   SUB - PANEL

SIZE of PANEL and FEEDER CABLE REQUIRED

Section 8 of the code has nothing to say about minimum sizes for a 2nd panel in a single family dwelling. We cannot apply Rule 8-200 to a sub-panel because that rule must be applied to the whole house, not just to a part of the load, and it sets the minimum size at 60 amps. This rule cannot, therefore, be properly applied to our sub-feeder.

However, all is not lost. We may apply a thumb rule to arrive at satisfactory sizes.
The "Thumb Rule" goes like this:

For **any size** house up to approximately 4000 sq. ft. floor area the following is usually acceptable.

EXAMPLE   1

Lighting Loads Only - if the 2nd panel will supply only lighting loads:

Sub-feeder Size	= #10 copper loomex cable. 30 amp fuses or circuit breakers in the main panel.
Sub-panel Size	= 8 or 12 circuit panel. We may have as many as we wish. This is usually governed by the number of outlets per circuit and the area served. Make sure your panel is large enough for the present load and for some future load additions.

EXAMPLE   2

Kitchen Electrical Loads - if the 2nd panel supplies lights and plugs in the kitchen area as well as other loads such as the garburator, dishwasher compactor etc. but not the electric range or dryer or electric heating in that area:

Sub-feeder Size	= #8 copper loomex cable. 50 amp fuses or circuit breakers.
Sub-panel Size	= 12 or more circuit panel is recommended. It is better to have too many circuit spaces for what you need now than to have too few spaces for your loads.

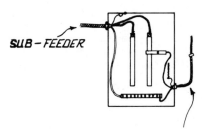

SUB–FEEDER

ONE BRANCH CIRCUIT SHOWN

CONNECT THE BLACK & RED WIRES TO THE BUSES.

THE WHITE WIRE CONNECTS TO THE NEUTRAL BUS.

THERE SHOULD BE NO CONNECTION BETWEEN THE NEUTRAL BUS AND THE METAL ENCLOSURE – NO BONDING SCREW.

THE BARE WIRE CONNECTS TO THE ENCLOSURE AT EACH END. THIS IS AN IMPORTANT CONNECTION. ALL GROUNDING FOR THE BRANCH CIRCUITS DEPEND ON THESE CONNECTIONS.

NOTE 1 **The range, dryer, and electric heating loads** are not normally supplied from the 2nd panel. These loads are usually supplied directly from the main service panel.

NOTE 2 **For a Garage Panel** - see under "Garage Wiring" on page 101.

NOTE 3 **Additions & Renovations to an Existing House** - see page 107 for more details.

(e) **Location** – Rule 6–210, 2–122

The service equipment shall be **inside** the building served.

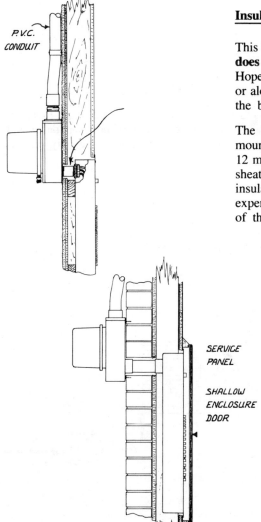

P.V.C. CONDUIT

SERVICE PANEL

SHALLOW ENCLOSURE DOOR

Insulation Required – Bulletin 6–8–0

This bulletin applies to service box installations in the colder areas of our Province. It **does not** apply to services installed in houses in the Fraser Valley anywhere up to Hope. Nor does it apply to service installations on Vancouver Island, the Gulf Islands or along the Sunshine Coast. The District of Terrace has a mild climate and therefore the bulletin does not apply there either.

The bulletin does apply to all other areas of the Province. If the service panel is mounted **in** an outside wall, not a partition, the bulletin requires a **minimum** 12 mm(½ in.) thick building insulation between the service panel and the exterior sheathing. Better be honest – the bulletin will allow a 12 mm air space without any insulation. This may result in excessive condensation in the service panel and expensive trouble in the future. Better to provide insulation. Best of all, is to stay out of that outside wall altogether. Locate the panel in a partition.

Accessible – The service panel should be mounted in a free wall where it will remain accessible. It should not be located above freezers, washers, dryers, tubs, etc. It should not be on the back wall of a storage room where access may become difficult due to stored items, nor should it be in bathrooms, clothes closets, stairwells, kitchen cabinets or similar places. Rules 6–210(1)(a), 2–308 and Bulletin 2–7–0.

Where such equipment is flush mounted in a wall, a covering door or frame may be installed over the equipment for appearance sake. This cabinet would be very shallow, providing no storage space for other items. Sometimes a calender or large picture is hung over the panel. This always provides a certain amount of excitement when a fuse blows, all the lights go out and you have to look under calenders and pictures to find the service panel.

(f) <u>**Height**</u> — Rules 6-210(1)(a), 14-106, 26-442(2), Bulletin 2-7-0

Minimum height above floor = 1.2 m(47.2 in.)

Approximate height to the center of the panel = 1600 mm(63 in.)

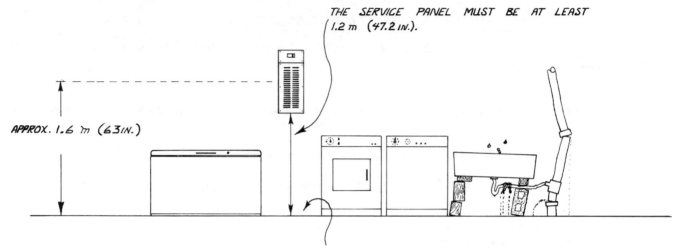

THE SERVICE PANEL MUST BE AT LEAST 1.2 m (47.2 IN.).

APPROX. 1.6 m (63 IN.)

THIS FLOOR AREA 1 m (39.4 IN.) IN FRONT OF THE PANEL MUST BE KEPT CLEAR. THE SERVICE PANEL MAY NOT BE LOCATED ABOVE ANY APPLIANCES OR COUNTERS OR SIMILAR OBJECT.

(g) <u>**Positioning**</u>

Service panelboards should be mounted in a vertical position.

Rule 14-110 was deleted in the new code. This rule required panels to be mounted in a vertical position. This rule was deleted to take into account the larger panels permitted by Rule 26-440. Panels may now have 60 or more circuit breakers. This will mean a corresponding increase in panel length so that in some cases it may be difficult to comply with the minimum 47 in. height required and still keep the top breakers properly accessible without having to stand on a chair to reach them. In these cases, mounting the panel in a **horizontal** position may be the only practical solution.

Please note − Most **fused** service switches may **not** be mounted upside down or on their side. Rule 14-502.

(h) <u>**Arrangement of Conductors**</u> − Rule 6-216, 12-3038

(i)   Service conductors and service ground may not enter the branch circuit section.

(ii)   Branch circuits of any kind may not enter the mains section.

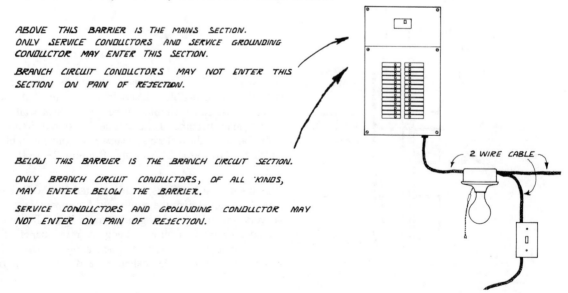

ABOVE THIS BARRIER IS THE MAINS SECTION. ONLY SERVICE CONDUCTORS AND SERVICE GROUNDING CONDUCTOR MAY ENTER THIS SECTION.

BRANCH CIRCUIT CONDUCTORS MAY NOT ENTER THIS SECTION ON PAIN OF REJECTION.

BELOW THIS BARRIER IS THE BRANCH CIRCUIT SECTION.

ONLY BRANCH CIRCUIT CONDUCTORS, OF ALL KINDS, MAY ENTER BELOW THE BARRIER.

SERVICE CONDUCTORS AND GROUNDING CONDUCTOR MAY NOT ENTER ON PAIN OF REJECTION.

2 WIRE CABLE

(i)   Grounding – Rule 10-106

(i)   **The object of grounding** the electrical wiring and equipment in your house is to reduce the possibility of electrical shock and fire damage. This is a very important part of your installation.

(ii)   **Rule Change -** Supplementary Ground Rods.

Rule 10-700 has been greatly revised. This rule now says that whenever we have at least 10ft. (3 m) of **metallic** water **service** pipe entering a single family house we **must** use that metal pipe as the service ground electrode and we do not need to install additional ground rods to supplement it. Remember, this applies only to the **water service pipe,** not to any other underground pipe you may have. The underground metallic water piping system is now considered sufficient without any additional rods. The thinking is that any additional ground rods would add very little to the grounding effectiveness of a metallic water piping system which is 10 or more feet long.

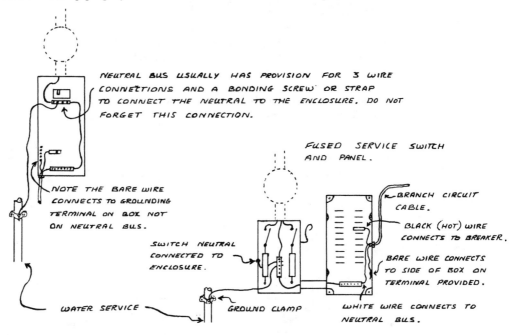

(iii)   **Main Switch** – Rule 10-204 states that the service neutral shall be connected to the service ground in the service switch or main circuit breaker compartment as shown above.

(iv)   **Caution - Regional Differences.**

This is a controversial subject and therefore the rules may not be the same in all areas of the Province.

You may find that the requirment in your area is to install one or more ground rods to supplement the effectiveness of the metallic water piping system. Check with your Inspector before installing your grounding system.

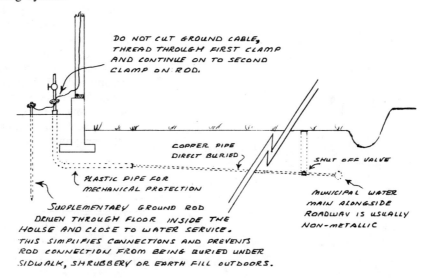

(v)   **Service Change in an Existing House**

Where the electrical service in an existing building is being changed you may not need to drive additional ground rods. Check the following:

1 - if the water service into the house is metallic and if the ground cable connection to this pipe is made in an approved manner; and

2 - if the size of the existing ground conductor will be large enough for the new service; and

3 - if the electrical rules in your area permit the use of the metallic water pipe as ground electrode without supplementary rods.

(vi)   **Plastic Water Service Pipe** - Rule 10-406(2)

Most new residential water services installed today are with plastic pipe. This means, of course, that we cannot use it as our grounding electrode. We must in these cases install an artificial grounding electrode. This usually consists of 2 - $^5/_8$ inch galvanized rods, 6 ft. long and driven into the ground at least 6 ft. apart.

The best place for these rods is inside the basement or crawlspace where it is much easier to keep them accessible as required by rule 10−904.

Don't forget the bonding requirement. Even if the water service is plastic pipe, the piping system **inside** the building may be **metallic**. If it is, it must be bonded to the ground rods, rule 10-406(2). This connection may be made at any convenient point on the cold water pipe where it will remain accessible.

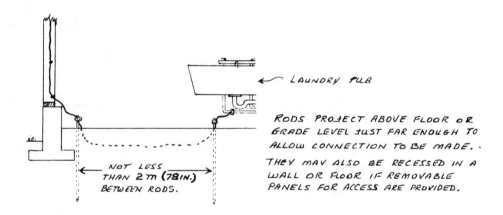

← LAUNDRY TUB

NOT LESS THAN 2 m (78 IN.) BETWEEN RODS.

RODS PROJECT ABOVE FLOOR OR GRADE LEVEL JUST FAR ENOUGH TO ALLOW CONNECTION TO BE MADE. THEY MAY ALSO BE RECESSED IN A WALL OR FLOOR IF REMOVABLE PANELS FOR ACCESS ARE PROVIDED.

(vi)   **Accessibility - Rules 10-902(2) & 10-904(2)**

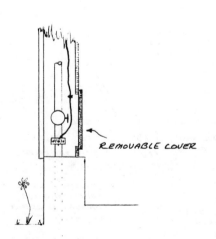

REMOVABLE COVER

Rule 10-902(2) says that if the electrical service is grounded to the incoming water service pipe, as described above, the connection must remain accessible wherever possible. Rule 10-904(2) says the same thing about the bonding points to water piping and ground rods. This means just what it says — leave it accessible. If the rods or the water pipe are located in a wall, provide an access panel as shown. Where the connections are a tripping hazard they may be recessed into the ground or concrete as shown.

SHORT SECTION OF PIPE WITH CAP OVER GROUND ROD.

(j) Ground Electrodes - Rule 10-702(7)&(9)(a)

Rule 10-702(7) sets minimum requirements for service grounding where the water piping system is of plastic or similar non−metallic material. The standard requirements, in most districts, are as follows:

two − ½ in. by 1800 mm(6 ft.) copper rods

two − ⅝ in. by 1800 mm(6 ft.) iron rods

Note − Driven **pipe** electrodes are **not approved** any longer.
− Electrodes shall be driven into the ground their full length.
− They shall be driven at least 2 m(6.6 ft.) apart and,
− They shall be connected together with a #6 or larger copper wire.

(i) Ufer Ground

Definition − These are also called concrete encased electrodes.

A Ufer ground consists of a single copper conductor, #4 or larger, encased in the concrete footings of the building. The copper conductor is thus in intimate contact with the concrete and thence with the earth under the footings. Properly installed these electrodes are very effective. Herein lies the key − to ensure an acceptable installation, your Inspector may want to see it before he will permit it to be covered. Check with your Inspector.

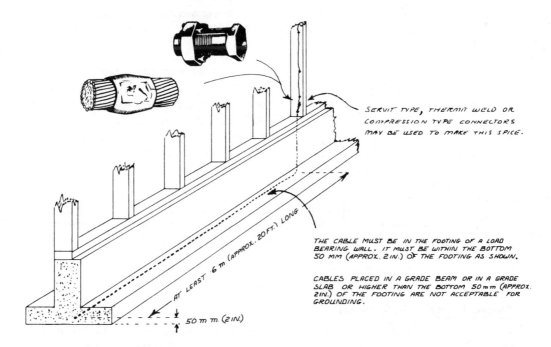

SERVIT TYPE, THERMIT WELD OR COMPRESSION TYPE CONNECTORS MAY BE USED TO MAKE THIS SPICE.

AT LEAST 6 m (APPROX. 20 FT.) LONG

50 m m. (2 IN.)

THE CABLE MUST BE IN THE FOOTING OF A LOAD BEARING WALL. IT MUST BE WITHIN THE BOTTOM 50 MM (APPROX. 2 IN.) OF THE FOOTING AS SHOWN.

CABLES PLACED IN A GRADE BEAM OR IN A GRADE SLAB OR HIGHER THAN THE BOTTOM 50 m m (APPROX. 2 IN.) OF THE FOOTING ARE NOT ACCEPTABLE FOR GROUNDING.

(ii) Conductor Required

Type −   must be copper.
must be bare.

Length −   must be at **least** 6 m(approx. 20 ft.) but may be much longer. This is the **horizontal** length of conductor along the base of the footing.

In addition to the 6 m. length of conductor run horizontally along the bottom 50 mm(approx. 2 in.) of the footing, you will require enough length to run up to the top of the foundation wall. Allow an additional 6 in.(approx. 150 mm) or so for connection to the service grounding conductor. See diagram above.

Note − The size of conductor required for this UFER ground is the same as that required for the grounding conductor by table 17 for services above 125 amps, therefore, it **may be**, but is not required to be, run **directly** to the service box.

Size —   For all service sizes up to and including 165 amp, the minimum conductor size is #4 bare copper.

For 200 amp service size use #3 bare copper.

Position —   must be in the footing.

Note — It is not correct to place this conductor in the floor slab or under it even if it is encased in concrete. The effectiveness of this electrode depends, in part, on the weight of the building to maintain intimate contact with earth under the footing.

Connection — Where the service grounding conductor must be connected to a UFER ground electrode, such connection may be made using a split bolt type connector as shown.

(iii)   Ground Cable — From service panel to grounding electrode.Rule 10-806

#6 Insulated
or Bare —

This cable may be used where it is not subject to mechanical injury. Wood moulding or plastic pipe may be used to protect those portions which are subject to mechanical injury. This cable may be used for grounding any service up to 125 amp.

#4 Insulated
or Bare —

If not exposed to severe mechanical injury, may be used for grounding any size service up to 165 amp. This is the most common service ground in use today.

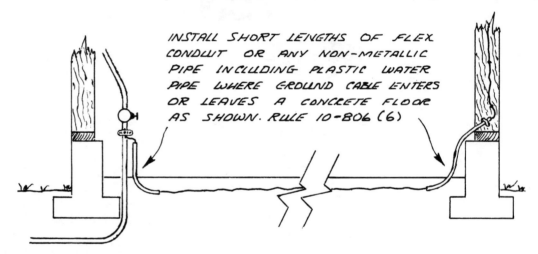

INSTALL SHORT LENGTHS OF FLEX. CONDUIT OR ANY NON-METALLIC PIPE INCLUDING PLASTIC WATER PIPE WHERE GROUND CABLE ENTERS OR LEAVES A CONCRETE FLOOR AS SHOWN. RULE 10-806 (6)

(k)   Ground Clamps - Rule 10-908

Make sure that the ground clamps you install are not only CSA certified but also that they are of **copper, bronze or brass.** The dry type connectors will not be approved in any outdoor location.

Where the ground clamps are in a consistantly dry location, such as in a dry crawl space or basement or located in a wall as shown under ''Accessibility'' one page back, the dry type clamp may be used. It's easy to get caught on this one - watch it.

(l)   Bonding

(i)   Service Switch — Rule 10-204 — All service equipment is provided with a brass bonding screw which must be installed to connect the neutral bus in the mains section to the metal enclosure. See sketch above under (i) Grounding.

(ii)   Gas Line — Rule 10-406(4) — The gas piping to the furnace, range, or dryer is now considered adequately grounded with the bare grounding grounding conductor in the supply cable to these appliances. Therefore, we do not require a separate grounding conductor to this piping system.

11. BRANCH CIRCUIT WIRING

(a) Overcurrent Protection

(i) Light and Plug Outlets − Rules 30−104, 14−600 − The maximum rating of fuse or breakers supplying lighting or branch circuits for plug outlets is 15 amp.

(ii) Appliance Plug Outlets − Rule 14−600 − The maximum rating of fuses or breakers supplying appliance plug outlets in kitchens and utility rooms is 15 amp. Throw away that 20 amp fuse or breaker − you need more circuits, not bigger fuses.

(iii) Range and Dryer Plug Outlets − Rule 26−746 requires plug outlets for these heavy appliances. See also page 83 under ''Heavy appliances''.

(iv) How Many Circuits − Rule 30−104 − Each circuit breaker or fuse may supply only one circuit. It is not correct to connect two or more wires to a circuit breaker or fuse. Rules 6−216, 8−108, 12−3000, 26−704. A sufficient number of breaker or fuse spaces should be provided in the service panel to comply with this requirement. See also page 30 under ''Service Panel''.

(v) Fuses − Rule 14−204 − Where fuse type panels are used it is difficult, if not impossible, to control the size of branch circuit fuses used. It is too easy to replace a blown fuse with one of a higher rating. To avoid this, all plug fuse holders must have a non−interchangeable adapter, as shown. Once a 15 amp adapter has been installed in this fuse base, the size of the opening and the thread is altered so that only a 15 amp fuse will now fit the base.

There is another less effective method of providing the non-interchangable feature. This consists of a reject washer which is inserted in the fuse socket in the panel. Each washer has a different size opening which will prevent a fuse of higher rating from making contact. The weakness with these washers is that they are too easily removed. They are CSA certified and may be installed. Who knows how long they remain in the sockets.

Reject Washer

PLUG FUSES—TYPE C

(b) Size of Cable

Use only #14 wire unless your runs are unusually long, say more than 30 m(approx. 100 ft.) long. The #12 wire is stiff. It can cause excessive strain on the switch and receptacle terminals.

3 Wire Cable − can save time and money − you are running two circuits in each cable. There may be a problem. If you are using a circuit breaker panelboardbe sure to install tie−bars on the handles of the breakers protecting these two circuits. This is to ensure that both circuits are de−energized for safety for anyone working on outlets served by either one of these circuits. If you are using a fuse panel you will need a special fuse block and fuse pull for each 3−wire cable entering the panel.

For heavy appliance wiring, look under specific type.

(c) Type of Cable

Rule 30−412 − All ceiling light outlet boxes must be wired with 90 degree C. wire. This is known as NMD7 or NMD-90. Thismeans that every wire entering a ceiling light outlet box must be NMD7 or NMD-90.

Cold Regions − Rule 12-102, Bulletin 12−3−0 − Thermoplastic insulated cables such as NMD7 or NMD-90 cable can be seriously damaged if it is flexed at temperatures lower than −10 degrees C (14 degrees F). Do not install cables in cold temperatures unless the cable is specifically approved for use at that temperature.

(d) Cable Strapping - Rule 12-610

Loomex cable should be strapped within 300 mm(12 in.) of the outlet box and approximately every 1.5 m(59 in.) throughout the run.

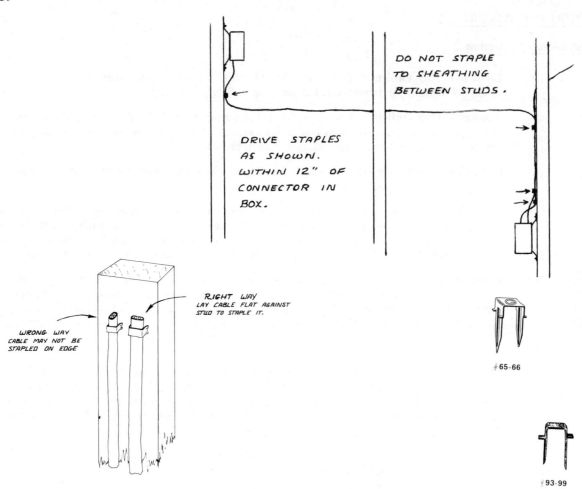

DO NOT STAPLE
TO SHEATHING
BETWEEN STUDS.

DRIVE STAPLES
AS SHOWN.
WITHIN 12" OF
CONNECTOR IN
BOX.

RIGHT WAY
LAY CABLE FLAT AGAINST
STUD TO STAPLE IT.

WRONG WAY
CABLE MAY NOT BE
STAPLED ON EDGE

#65-66

#93-99

Caution

1 - Do not staple 2 wire cable on edge − they must lie flat. See rule 12−606(5). This applies to two wire cables only.

2 - Do not overdrive the staples. Drive staples only until they contact the cable sheath − don't squish the cable. Because the cables are scantily dressed (insulated) the installers must be more careful when handling and strapping it.

3 - Rule 2−108 − Be sure to use the correct size staple or strap for each size cable. It is not correct to use a 2−wire cable strap on a 3−wire cable or vice−versa unless the staple or strap is specifically approved for both sizes, nor is it correct to put two cables under a single strap or staple.

4 - Where cables are run along studs or joists they should be kept at least 1¼ in. from the nailing edge. Between staples the cable is free to move aside should a drywallers nail miss the stud but at the point of the staple the cable is held captive. If the cable has been stapled too close to the edge of a stud or joist it really needs protection. There is no code rule which specifically requires this protection except that Rule 2-108 says poor workmanship will not be accepted by the inspection department. It is best to run your cables along the middle, or as near the middle, of the stud or joist wherever possible and provide additional protection where it is not possible to run it there.

(e) Cable Protection - Rule 12-616

(i)   Where the cable is run through holes in studs, plates or joists, these holes shall be at least 32 mm(1¼ in.) from the edge of the wood member.

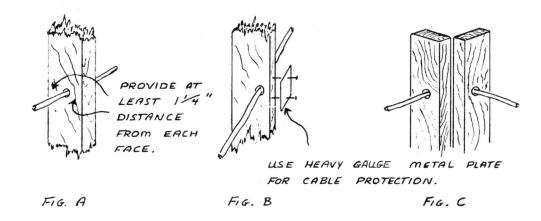

PROVIDE AT LEAST 1¼" DISTANCE FROM EACH FACE.

USE HEAVY GAUGE METAL PLATE FOR CABLE PROTECTION.

FIG. A   FIG. B   FIG. C

(ii)   In the case of small dimension members such as may be used in partition walls, the cable hole should be located so that there is 32 mm(1¼ in.) clearance on one side. Fig.B. To protect the other side use a minimum #14 gauge metal plate (the side of a metal outlet box does this job very well). This must be done in every case where the 32 mm(1¼in.) clearance cannot otherwise be obtained. In corners of rooms, as in Fig.C. the holes may need to be drilled on an angle providing less than the minimum distance — here too, use heavy metal plates.

Holes may contain more than one cable but must be large enough to prevent damage to the cable sheath during installation.

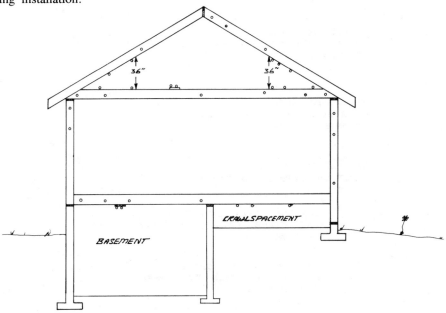

RUN THROUGH HOLES IN JOISTS OR STUDS OR PROVIDE PROTECTION FOR THE CABLE WITH A RUNNING BOARD AS SHOWN.

(iii)   **Exposed Cable** — Rule 12−618 — Where loomex cable is run on the **surface** of the wall and within 1.5 m(59 in.) from the floor, as is often the case in buildings of solid wall construction, the cable shall be protected from mechanical damage with wood or similar moulding.

(iv)   **Hot Air Ducts or**
Hot Water Pipes — Rule 12−606(4) requires loomex cable to be kept at least 25 mm(1 in.) away from all hot air heating ducts and hot water piping. A chunk of building insulation may be placed between the cable and the duct or pipe, as shown.

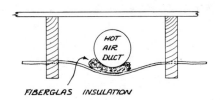

FIBERGLAS INSULATION

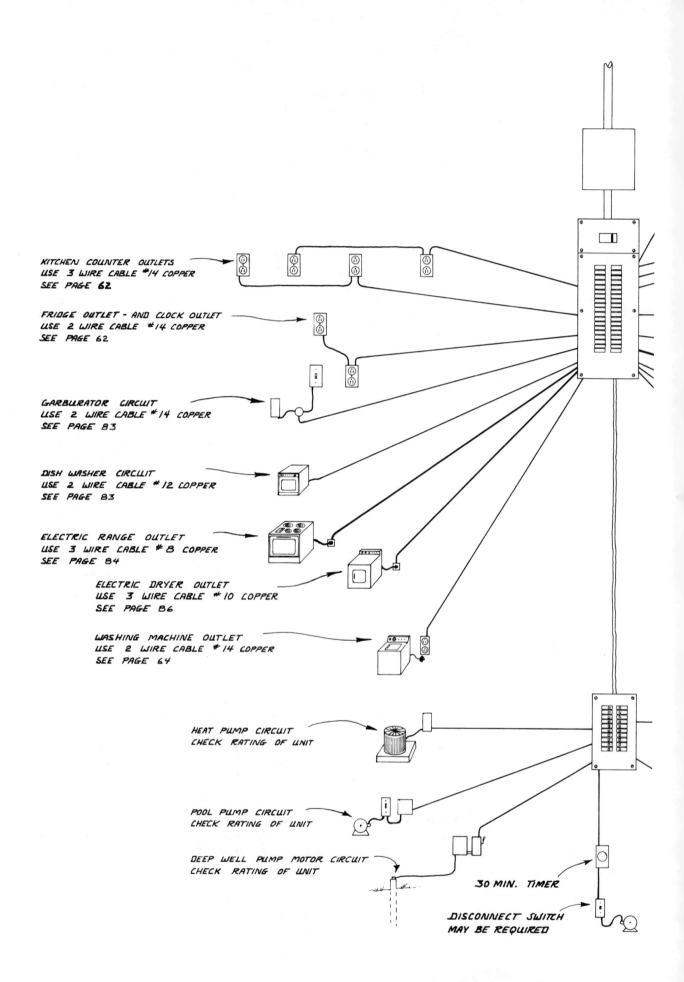

KITCHEN COUNTER OUTLETS
USE 3 WIRE CABLE #14 COPPER
SEE PAGE 62

FRIDGE OUTLET - AND CLOCK OUTLET
USE 2 WIRE CABLE #14 COPPER
SEE PAGE 62

GARBURATOR CIRCUIT
USE 2 WIRE CABLE #14 COPPER
SEE PAGE 83

DISH WASHER CIRCUIT
USE 2 WIRE CABLE #12 COPPER
SEE PAGE 83

ELECTRIC RANGE OUTLET
USE 3 WIRE CABLE #8 COPPER
SEE PAGE 84

ELECTRIC DRYER OUTLET
USE 3 WIRE CABLE #10 COPPER
SEE PAGE 86

WASHING MACHINE OUTLET
USE 2 WIRE CABLE #14 COPPER
SEE PAGE 64

HEAT PUMP CIRCUIT
CHECK RATING OF UNIT

POOL PUMP CIRCUIT
CHECK RATING OF UNIT

DEEP WELL PUMP MOTOR CIRCUIT
CHECK RATING OF UNIT

30 MIN. TIMER

DISCONNECT SWITCH
MAY BE REQUIRED

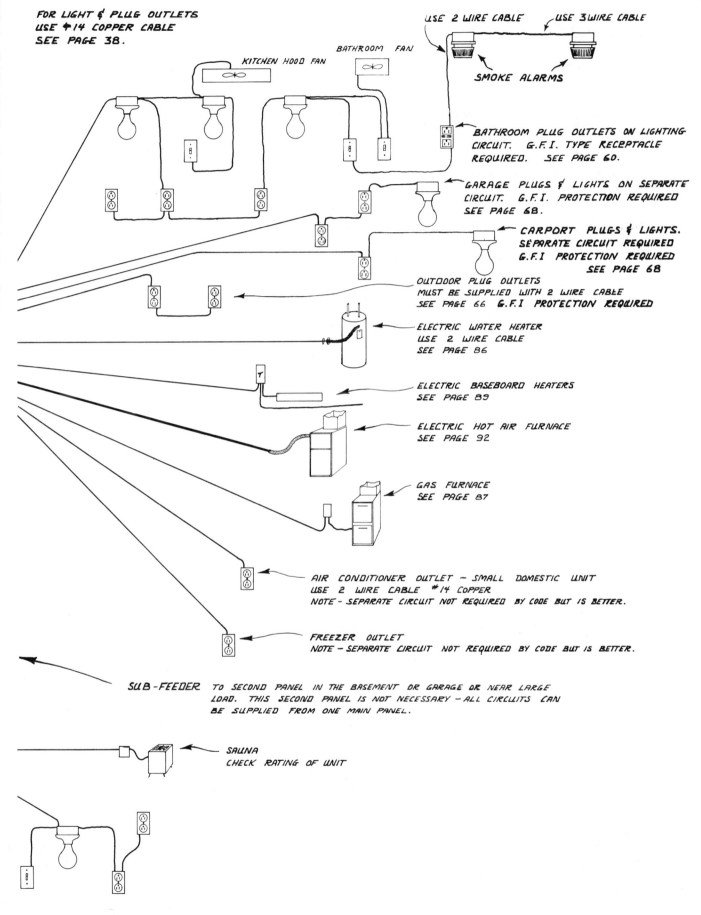

FOR LIGHT & PLUG OUTLETS
USE #14 COPPER CABLE
SEE PAGE 38.

USE 2 WIRE CABLE   USE 3 WIRE CABLE

KITCHEN HOOD FAN

BATHROOM FAN

SMOKE ALARMS

BATHROOM PLUG OUTLETS ON LIGHTING
CIRCUIT. G.F.I. TYPE RECEPTACLE
REQUIRED.   SEE PAGE 60.

GARAGE PLUGS & LIGHTS ON SEPARATE
CIRCUIT. G.F.I. PROTECTION REQUIRED
SEE PAGE 68.

CARPORT PLUGS & LIGHTS.
SEPARATE CIRCUIT REQUIRED
G.F.I PROTECTION REQUIRED
            SEE PAGE 68

OUTDOOR PLUG OUTLETS
MUST BE SUPPLIED WITH 2 WIRE CABLE
SEE PAGE 66 G.F.I PROTECTION REQUIRED

ELECTRIC WATER HEATER
USE 2 WIRE CABLE
SEE PAGE 86

ELECTRIC BASEBOARD HEATERS
SEE PAGE 89

ELECTRIC HOT AIR FURNACE
SEE PAGE 92

GAS FURNACE
SEE PAGE 87

AIR CONDITIONER OUTLET — SMALL DOMESTIC UNIT
USE 2 WIRE CABLE #14 COPPER
NOTE — SEPARATE CIRCUIT NOT REQUIRED BY CODE BUT IS BETTER.

FREEZER OUTLET
NOTE — SEPARATE CIRCUIT NOT REQUIRED BY CODE BUT IS BETTER.

SUB-FEEDER TO SECOND PANEL IN THE BASEMENT OR GARAGE OR NEAR LARGE
LOAD. THIS SECOND PANEL IS NOT NECESSARY — ALL CIRCUITS CAN
BE SUPPLIED FROM ONE MAIN PANEL.

SAUNA
CHECK RATING OF UNIT

HYDROMASSAGE BATHTUB
SEPARATE G.F.I PROTECTED
CIRCUIT REQUIRED

12.　OUTLET BOXES

(a)　Outlets per Circuit — Rule 12-3000

A maximum of 12 outlets may be connected to a circuit. This may consist of 12 light outlets or 12 plug outlets (not appliance plugs, see page 61 for appliance plugs) or any combination of light and plug outlets mixed, as long as their total number does not exceed 12 outlets.

It is better to have the load consist of a mixture of lights and plugs. This gives better load diversity on the circuit and less chance of a complete blackout in case of circuit failure.

To avoid confusion and costly duplication proceed as follows:

(i)　Make a floor plan of your house. If more than one floor, draw a separate plan for each floor.

(ii)　Show each outlet using the symbols given below.

(iii)　Determine best location for service equipment.

(iv)　Draw a line showing the course each cable run will take. Start with one circuit and complete it before going on to the next. Identify each **circuit** and each **outlet** for quick easy location. For example, the outlets on the first circuit would be A1, A2, A3 etc. The outlets on circuit B would be B1, B2, B3 etc.

Symbols usually used are:

◯　light outlet on ceiling

─◯　wall outlet, such as over a bathroom vanity.

S　wall switch

S_3　three-way switch

S_4　four-way switch

⦶　duplex plug receptacle

⦶　split duplex receptacle, used above kitchen counter, see page 61

(b)　Light Outlet Boxes — Rule 2-314

Illumination is required by code only at the service equipment for maintenance purposes. There is no rule which says you must have light outlets in any other area of the house. Obviously, the best time to install extra light, switch and plug outlets is in the rough wiring stage — it's a lot less expensive then.

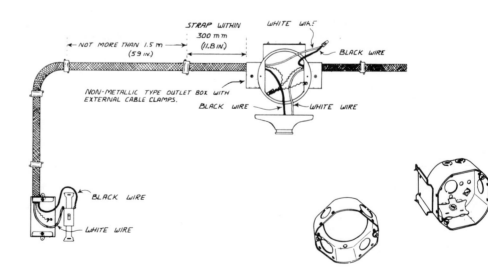

(c) **Recessed Light Outlet** — Rules 30—308, 30—410

NON - Insulated areas

Watch this one carefully. If there is any possibility of building insulation being placed near this fixture the Inspector will reject it unless it is a specifically approved fixture and has a large heat box over it or it is a fixture which is specifically approved for covering with building insulation. Both of these methods are illustrated below. Ceilings which have a living floor area above, such as a basement or first floor ceiling in a two story house, are usually not insulated. In these cases a standard CSA certified recessed light fixture may be used without the ugly coffin box above it.

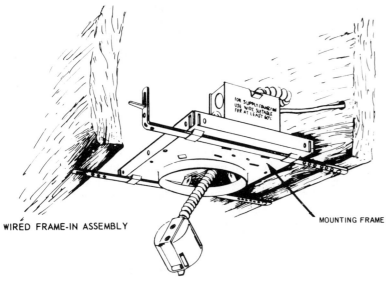

WIRED FRAME-IN ASSEMBLY

MOUNTING FRAME

Pre—Wired Type — Most recessed light fixtures used today are pre—wired type. This fixture has a short length of high temperature wire connecting the fixture to a connection box. The supply cable may run directly into the connection box as shown below.

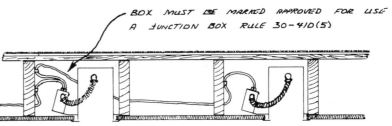

BOX MUST BE MARKED APPROVED FOR USE AS A JUNCTION BOX RULE 30-410(5)

The illustration shows a second floor above the recessed light fixture. In this case there is no requirement for building insulation and therefore, the heat dissipator box shown below is not required. However, this fixture can still be a fire hazard if the minimum ½ in. clearance from wood is not maintained all around and on top of the fixture. The only points where the ½ in. clearance is not required is where the ceiling butts up against the fixture and at the support points around the lower edge.

INSULATED Ceilings

If you plan to install recessed light fixtures in an **insulated** ceiling you may use the standard type recessed fixture in a heat box, as described below, or you may use a specially designed fixture which is CSA certified for covering with building insulation.

SPECIALLY DESIGNED FIXTURE

This is a specially designed fixture which is enclosed in a metal box. It **does not require a heat box** it may be covered with building insulation.

Wattage Rating - At present fixtures certified for covering with building insulation are limited to max. 75 watt lamps.

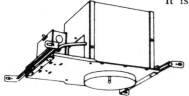

It is hoped the industry will soon have fixtures which are certified for 150 watts or more.

This fixture is equipped with a built-in thermostat to shut itself off in case it overheats. Some homeowners have installed 150 watt lamps in these fixtures. It works fine, for a few moments until the higher wattage lamp overheats the fixture. At this point the thermostat shuts it off. When it cools it turns itself back on again. Obviously, it could not do this for very long. The thermostat is not designed for repeated on off switching, it would very soon fail. Make sure you use the correct size lamp in your fixture.

STANDARD RECESSED LIGHT FIXTURES

Fire Hazard

A number of fires have been caused by incorrectly installed recessed light fixtures. Bulletin 30−1−0 requires that a heat dissipator box be built over each recessed light fixture (unless it is certified for direct covering) to keep it from overheating. This box is required over every recessed light fixture which could be blanketed with building insulation. The question is not, do you plan to insulate in the fixture area but rather, is it possible to apply insulation there − − − − − − even with some difficulty. The Inspector is working to make your home safe. Because these fixtures can be a fire hazard you really want him to be very careful.

The insulation does exactly what it is supposed to do − it traps the heat in the fixture. When the fixture reaches the combustion temperature of the wood or paper next to it we could have a fire.

To eliminate this fire hazard the bulletin requires a large box to be built over the fixture as shown below. This box may be covered with building insulation. The heat generated by the lamp can apparently be dissipated through the large surface area of this enclosure.

HEAT BOX - for 24 in. joist space.

Make sure you have sufficient clearance here to provide the dimensions required by bulletin 30−1−0. See page 45 for dimensions of heat dissipator boxes required by this bulletin.

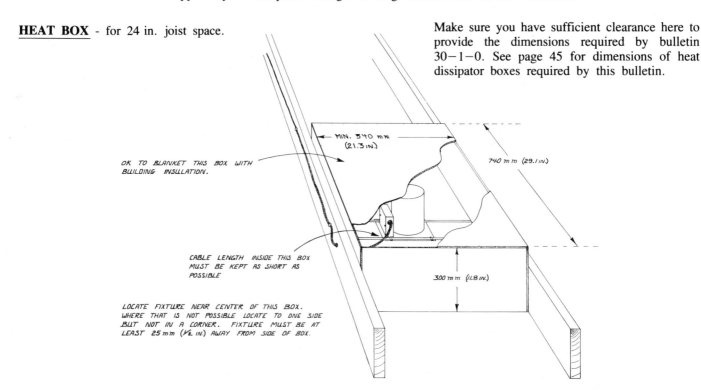

Note − The Electrical Inspector will insist on a minimum 11.8 in. in depth for the heat dissipator box because that is what the bulletin requires. The Building Inspector will insist on a minimum insulation above that box. This means that in some cases it will be impossible to install a recessed light fixture. Check carefully the proposed location of the recessed light fixture for all clearances required.

HEAT BOX -for 16 in. joist space.

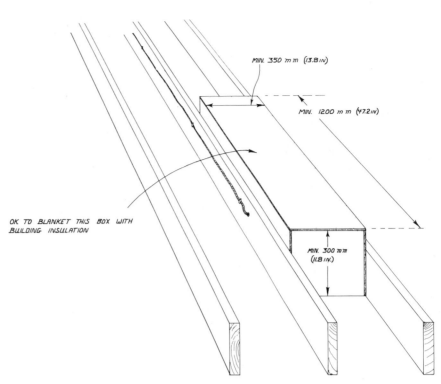

MIN. 350 mm (13.8 IN.)

MIN. 1200 mm (47.2 IN.)

MIN. 300 mm (11.8 IN.)

OK TO BLANKET THIS BOX WITH BUILDING INSULATION

Combination Heat Lamp and Fan Fixtures - These must also be enclosed in a heat dissipator box as shown. There is an exception, if the fixture is **marked certified for use in thermal insulation** the large box is not required.

<u>**Box Dimensions**</u> - Bulletin 30-1-0(3)

The dimensions given are minimum — we may not change these except to make them larger. We may not use a smaller dimension than the minimum given, even if we increase another dimension to provide for the same minimum **cubic volume**. The bulletin refers to minimum **dimensions** not minimum **volume**.

Inside or Outside Measurements — Unfortunately, the bulletin does not indicate this information. Obviously it does not matter unless the box is built of very thick material.

Note — Acceptable Fixtures — Not all recessed lighting fixtures are acceptable for installation in this box. Consult with your Inspector who has a list of these recessed light fixtures which have been especially tested by CSA for mounting in this box. Don't attempt to use any other type.

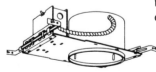

<u>**Location of Fixture in Box**</u>

Place the fixture near the center of the box if at all possible. If it cannot be centered it should not be closer than 25 mm(0.98 in.) from the side of the box.

Note — Keep all other wiring out of this box.

Note — Where this fixture is equipped with a large heat dissipator box, as described below, only the supply cable to the fixture may enter the large enclosure. Keep all other cables for other outlets out of the heat box.

Connection Box − The connection box on the fixture may be used only for the supply conductors to this one light fixture. You may not use it as a junction box for any other loads **unless it is approved for that purpose**. You will find many of these fixtures are equipped with boxes which are certified for use as a junction box. If they are acceptable for use as a junction box they will be so marked.

(d) <u>**Fluorescent Light Outlets**</u> − Rules 12−606(1), 12−3002(5), 30−312(3) & Bulletins 12−11−0 & 30-2-0

Loomex cable may be run directly into a fluorescent light fixture as shown. Where fluorescent fixtures are mounted end to end as in valance or cornice lighting, the loomex cable should enter only the first fixture. The interconnecting wires between fixtures must be R90 or better.

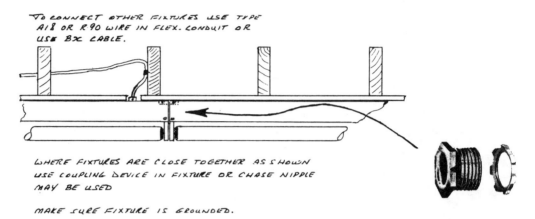

TO CONNECT OTHER FIXTURES USE TYPE A18 OR R90 WIRE IN FLEX. CONDUIT OR USE BX CABLE.

WHERE FIXTURES ARE CLOSE TOGETHER AS SHOWN USE COUPLING DEVICE IN FIXTURE OR CHASE NIPPLE MAY BE USED

MAKE SURE FIXTURE IS GROUNDED.

That threaded thing with a locknut next to it, in the illustration, is called a chase bushing. Punch out the knockout holes in the end of the fixtures where they join. The fixtures are then fastened to the ceiling with their ends as close together as possible. The chase nipple is now inserted through the two knockouts and the locknut is used to bring the two fixture end plates together for grounding. This chase bushing also provides a smooth throat to protect the fixture supply conductors.

<u>**Outlet Box Not Required**</u>

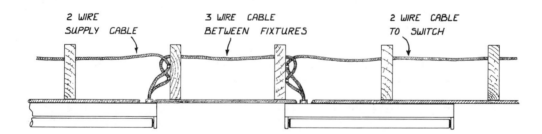

2 WIRE SUPPLY CABLE

3 WIRE CABLE BETWEEN FIXTURES

2 WIRE CABLE TO SWITCH

As shown, the loomex cable is run directly into the fixture. An outlet box is not required provided the cable used is NMD7 or NMD-90 and not more than two cables enter any fixture.

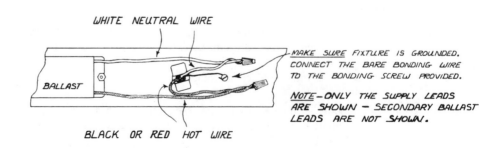

WHITE NEUTRAL WIRE

BALLAST

BLACK OR RED HOT WIRE

MAKE SURE FIXTURE IS GROUNDED. CONNECT THE BARE BONDING WIRE TO THE BONDING SCREW PROVIDED.

NOTE—ONLY THE SUPPLY LEADS ARE SHOWN − SECONDARY BALLAST LEADS ARE NOT SHOWN.

(e) Bathroom Light Outlets – Rule 62-114(1)(b) Bulletin 30-2-0 and 62-1-0

Heat Lamps – Like any other recessed light fixture, heat lamps can be a very real fire hazard if improperly installed. Care should be taken to:

(i) Locate the fixture away from the door so that it cannot radiate heat directly onto the upper edge of the door when it is in the open position. This applies to the shower stall doors as well as the bathroom entry door. The Bulletin also requires that you keep the heat lamp fixture at least 12in. away from the shower rod if there is one. Unfortunately the Bulletin is not clear on this point but it would seem logical this distance is to be horizontal not vertical.

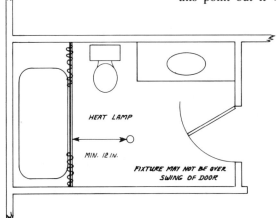

The reason for all this is to eliminate a possible fire hazard. The upper edge of the door would be too close to the fixture and could become overheated. The shower rod could be used to hang towels and clothing. They could become overheated if they were under the heat lamp. Keep the heat lamp at least 12in. away from the shower rod. This is a **horizontal** measurement.

(ii) install a heat dissipating box over the fixture as described on page 45.

Swag Lamps – Rule 10–516(2) – Be sure to use the correct fixture – it must have a ground conductor to each chain–hung lamp holder.

(f) Clothes Closet Light Outlets – Rule 30–204(1)

Light outlet boxes in closets may be in the ceiling or on the front wall above the door.

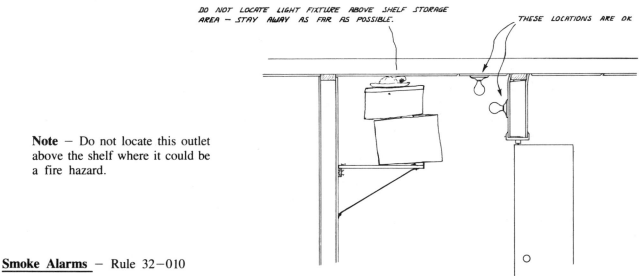

Note – Do not locate this outlet above the shelf where it could be a fire hazard.

Smoke Alarms – Rule 32–010

The National Building Code requires smoke alarm devices in each residential dwelling unit.

(i) **How Many Required** – The rule says they 'shall be installed between each sleeping area and the remainder of the dwelling unit; and where the sleeping areas are served by hallways, the smoke alarms shall be installed in the hallway'. All the bedrooms facing onto a common hallway could be served with one device, however, bedrooms on another floor or in the basement are in another 'area' and would therefore require another device. The number of smoke alarm units required for your house, and the location of these devices is controlled by the local Builing Inspector or Fire Officer.

(ii) **Outlet Box Required** — Use a standard light outlet box mounted as for a light outlet. This box may also be used as a junction box to serve other loads — it need not be at the end of a run.

(iii) **Position** — The rule says the smoke alarm shall be installed 'on or near the ceiling' depending on the installation instructions that come with the device.

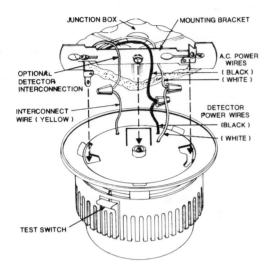

Circuit Required — May be supplied with any **lighting** circuit or plug outlet circuit (except those circuits which supply kitchen plug outlets, laundry and outdoor plug outlets).

Note — Do **not** switch this outlet. It must **not** be possible to turn this thing off except with the breaker in the panel.

(iv) 2 or More Smoke Alarms — Where two or more smoke alarms are installed the rule says they must all operate together — that is, if one alarm is activated to sound an alarm the others must all be connected together so that they all automatically sound the alarm together. Actually the electrical code does not require this but National Building Code does.

Smoke alarm devices are not all the same. Some manufacturers design their devices for L.V. (low voltage) wiring method between alarm units, while others are designed for line voltage. Units designed for L.V. wiring method may have the interconnecting wiring between units with type LVT cable.

Units designed for line voltage (120 volts) usually require three wire #14 loomex cable between units. The third conductor is for the signal circuit, the other two are required to supply power to the second and third units. This type is in common use today.

Overhead Fans

These fans are becoming more and more popular. They not only look smart they also serve a usefull purpose by moving the heated air downward to the floor level.

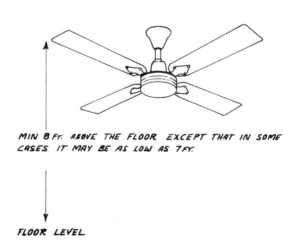

MIN 8 FT. ABOVE THE FLOOR EXCEPT THAT IN SOME CASES IT MAY BE AS LOW AS 7 FT.

FLOOR LEVEL

Some things to watch for:

(1) Look for a CSA or BC Government certification label. Never purchase any electrical appliance unless it is clearly marked with a CSA or BC Government certification label. This is your protection and assurance that the device has been checked against a good standard.

(2) Look for mounting instructions. Each fan has a caution marking which gives the minimum mounting height above floor required for that particular fan. This marking will look somthing like this;

Caution: Mount with the lowest mounting parts at least 8 ft. above floor or grade level.

Some fans will not turn as fast at maximum speed or the fan blades are designed so they are less hazardous to anyone coming in accedental contact with the blades. These fans will also have caution markings similar to the words given above except that in this case the minimum mounting height will be 7 ft. instead of 8 ft.. In this case the fan blades may be as low as 7 ft. above the floor.

Near Staiways, Balconies and such like.

The fan blades may not be within reach of a person standing on a stairway, a landing or a balcony. If the blades are within reach the minimum height given on the caution notice must be measured from the level the person is standing on.

It is usually easier to locate the fan outlet far enough away, at least 1 m (39.3 in.)., from the hand rail of a balcony or stairway. This detail is very important at the rough wiring stage.

Actually, this 39.3 in. distance is an arbitrary minimum distance I have chosen because I believe all inspectors would accept it. The code does not specify any distance here. Therefore the 39.3 in. distance is, I suppose, negotiable. Check with your Inspector.

Circuit required

This fan may be supplied with any lighting circuit which has only 11 or fewer outlets. The fan outlet, though it is a small load, counts as one outlet.

Caution; On Dec. 10th. 1986 CSA issued a news release regarding these fans. It warned that if the blades are not properly installed they may work loose and fall to the floor. Anyone in the path of such a flying blade could be seriously hurt.

(g) Switch Outlet Boxes

Height of Switches − The rules do not specify a required height for wall mounted light switches. They may be located at any convenient height − usually they are set at approximately 1.2 m(approx. 48 in.) to the lower edge of the box.

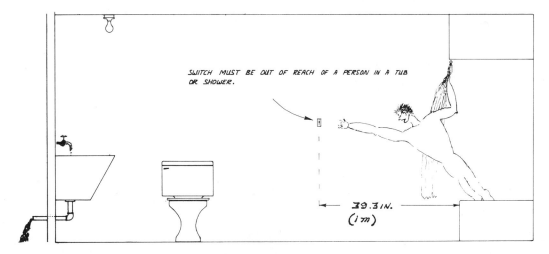

Bathroom Light, Heat Lamp and Fan Switches − Rule 30-326(3) says the light switch must not be located within reach of a person in a shower or bathtub. Bulletin 26-2-0-(5) defines out of reach as 39.3in. (1m). This means that switches controlling these loads **may** be in the bathroom provided they are at least 39.3in. from the nearest inside face of a bathtub or shower.

Note - This is a **horizontal** measurement from the switch to the nearest inside face of a tub or shower.

NOTE — Bulletin 26-2-0(5) says this applies to all switches **in bathrooms** including those for lights, fans, heat lamps and adjustable thermostats or switches for electric heaters.

Stairwell Light Switch — Rule 30-328 — Lamps which are used to light basement stairs shall be controlled by a switch located at a convenient spot above the stairs.

Connection of Switches — Rules 4-034(2), 30-604 — Switch connections shall be made so that there is a white wire and a black wire to the fixture. To do this the connection should be made as follows: The white wire in the supply cable shall connect directly to the screw shell (the silver terminal) in the lamp holder. The black wire from the switch connects to the center (gold) terminal in the lamp holder. In this way the fixture has a black and a white wire supplying it. It also has the black wire connected so that the screw base of the bulb cannot become energized. **This is very important.**

The following drawings illustrate acceptable methods of connection in switch and outlet boxes.

Simplest Switching Arrangement — Power entering light outlet box first.

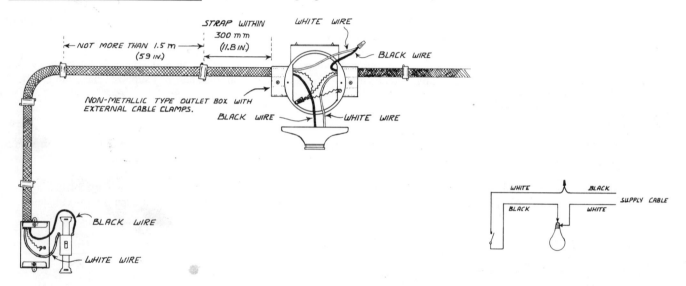

Power Entering Switch Outlet Box

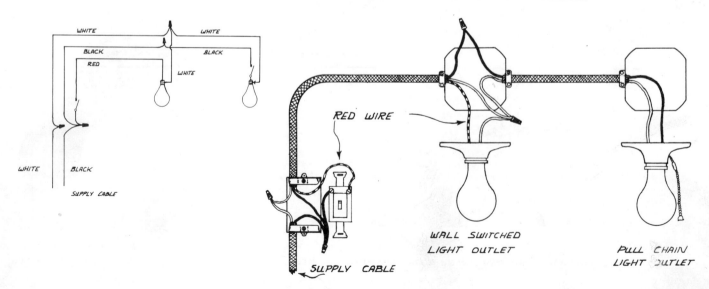

Power Feeding Through Switch Box to Receptacle Outlet

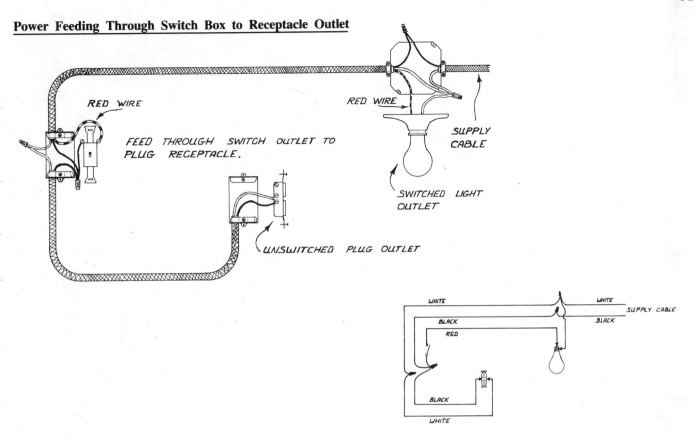

RED WIRE

FEED THROUGH SWITCH OUTLET TO PLUG RECEPTACLE.

RED WIRE

SUPPLY CABLE

SWITCHED LIGHT OUTLET

UNSWITCHED PLUG OUTLET

WHITE   WHITE
SUPPLY CABLE
BLACK   BLACK
RED

BLACK

WHITE

3 WAY SWITCHES

Both switches on one side of light outlet

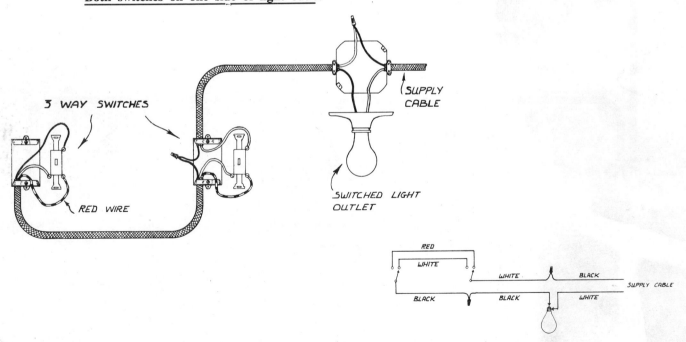

3 WAY SWITCHES

SUPPLY CABLE

RED WIRE

SWITCHED LIGHT OUTLET

RED
WHITE
WHITE   BLACK
SUPPLY CABLE
BLACK   BLACK   WHITE

Note - Rule 14-604 & Bulletin 14-4-0

The drawings for 3-way and 4-way switches show the cable entering the light outlet box first. Strictly speaking, this is what the rule requires. However, it is seldom applied that way. The new bulletin permits the supply cable to run first to any of the switch boxes. This means that your not stuck with the 3-way and 4-way switching arrangements shown but are able to vary it a little.

Light outlet between switches

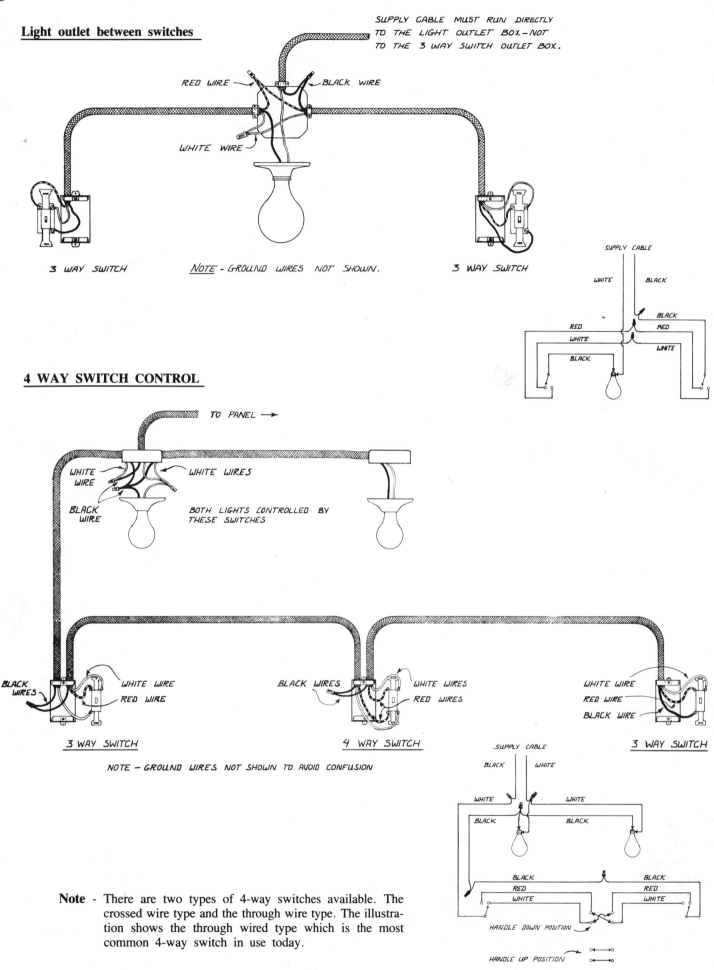

SUPPLY CABLE MUST RUN DIRECTLY
TO THE LIGHT OUTLET BOX.—NOT
TO THE 3 WAY SWITCH OUTLET BOX.

RED WIRE — BLACK WIRE

WHITE WIRE

3 WAY SWITCH   NOTE - GROUND WIRES NOT SHOWN.   3 WAY SWITCH

SUPPLY CABLE

WHITE   BLACK

RED   BLACK
WHITE   RED
BLACK   WHITE

4 WAY SWITCH CONTROL

TO PANEL →

WHITE WIRE   WHITE WIRES

BLACK WIRE   BOTH LIGHTS CONTROLLED BY THESE SWITCHES

BLACK WIRES   WHITE WIRE   BLACK WIRES   WHITE WIRES   WHITE WIRE
RED WIRE   RED WIRES   RED WIRE
BLACK WIRE

3 WAY SWITCH   4 WAY SWITCH   3 WAY SWITCH

NOTE - GROUND WIRES NOT SHOWN TO AVOID CONFUSION

SUPPLY CABLE
BLACK   WHITE

WHITE   WHITE
BLACK   BLACK

BLACK   BLACK
RED   RED
WHITE   WHITE

HANDLE DOWN POSITION

HANDLE UP POSITION

Note - There are two types of 4-way switches available. The crossed wire type and the through wire type. The illustration shows the through wired type which is the most common 4-way switch in use today.

2-Gang Switch box - switched plugs for living room or bedrooms.

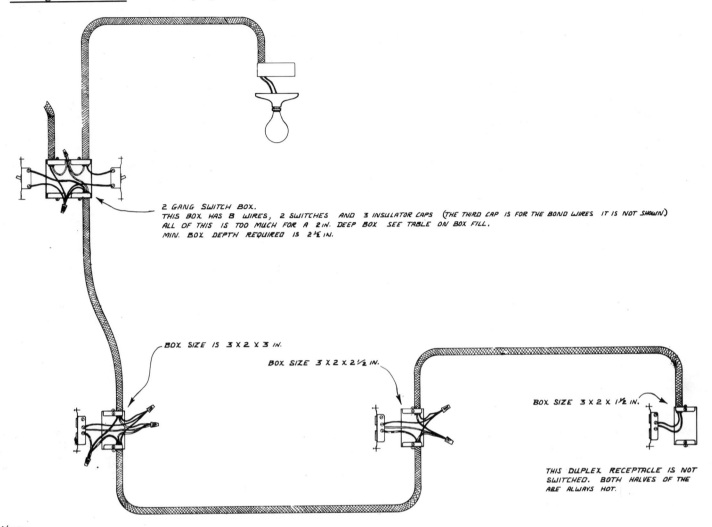

2 GANG SWITCH BOX.
THIS BOX HAS 8 WIRES, 2 SWITCHES AND 3 INSULATOR CAPS (THE THIRD CAP IS FOR THE BOND WIRES IT IS NOT SHOWN)
ALL OF THIS IS TOO MUCH FOR A 2 IN. DEEP BOX SEE TABLE ON BOX FILL.
MIN. BOX DEPTH REQUIRED IS 2½ IN.

BOX SIZE IS 3 X 2 X 3 IN.

BOX SIZE 3 X 2 X 2½ IN.

BOX SIZE 3 X 2 X 1½ IN.

THIS DUPLEX RECEPTACLE IS NOT SWITCHED. BOTH HALVES OF THE ARE ALWAYS HOT.

NOTE
THE BARE BOND WIRES ARE NOT SHOWN TO AVOID CONFUSION.

THE LOWER HALF OF THESE TWO RECEPTACLES ARE WALL SWITCHED. THE UPPER HALF OF EACH OUTLET IS NOT SWITCHED - IT IS ALWAYS HOT.

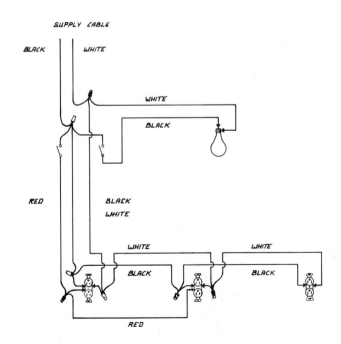

SUPPLY CABLE

BLACK   WHITE

WHITE

BLACK

RED

BLACK
WHITE

WHITE   WHITE

BLACK   BLACK

RED

The illustration shows a panel and 3 circuits.

It shows
- the box sizes required.
- the number of outlets permitted per circuit.
- the method of identifying outlets on plans.
- the type of fuse pull or breakers required for 3−wire cables.

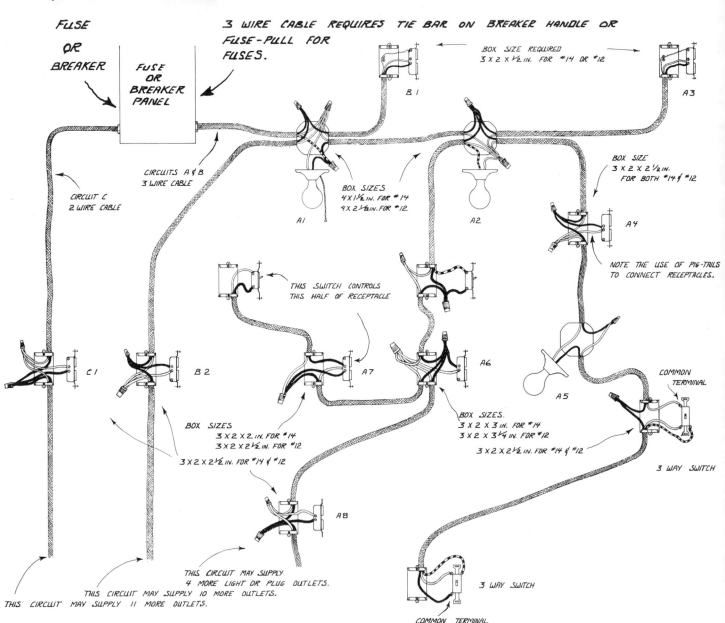

Note - Rule 14-010 Bulletin 26-2-0(9)

Circuits A & B are supplied with a 3−wire cable to the first outlet where it is split into 2−wire cables. Whenever we run a 3−wire cable **into the service panel** we must use tie−bars on the two breakers supplying these circuits or if you are using a fuse panel you will require a fuse pull, as shown. If you don't feel comfortable with this tacky requirement, then avoid it by using only 2−wire cables into the service panel. Don't forget, if you use only 2-wire cable it will take a lot more to do the job. This rule applies to 3−wire cables only if they are run into a panelboard − it does not apply to 3−wire cables anywhere else in the circuit.

(h) **Plug Outlets** — Rule 26-702 & Bulletin 26-2-0

(i) **Height** — The rules do not specify any definite height for plug outlets. They may be at any convenient height. Usually they are placed at approximately 300 mm(approx. 12 in.) to lower edge of the outlet box in the living room, dining room, bedrooms and hallways etc.

Horizontal or Vertical — may be either way but if you want a professional looking job, install them all in the vertical plane.

(ii) **How Many Plugs and Where Required**

Living room
Family room
Rec room
Bedroom
Den
Study

Rule 26-702(2)(3)&(4) requires plug outlets in these rooms to be located so that no electrical appliance located along the wall is more than 1.8 m(approx. 6 ft.) from such outlet

Note: This measurement is **not** a radius — you must measure into corners as shown in the illustration. This is the **strict** interpretation of sub-rule 2.

Notes Wall space **less** than 900 mm(approx. 36 in.) wide is not required to have an outlet.

— Do not count spaces occupied by:

(1) doorway, and the area occupied by the door when fully open.

(2) windows which are less than 11.8 in. (300 mm) above the floor.

(3) fireplaces.

(4) other permanently fixed installations which limit the use of wall space.

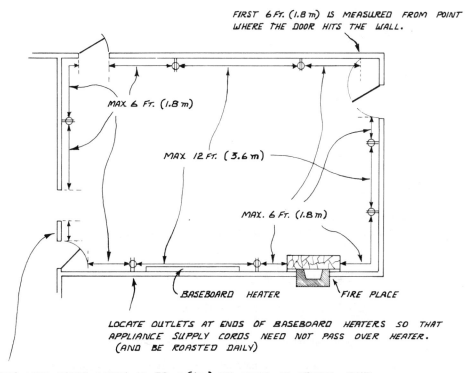

FIRST 6 FT. (1.8 m) IS MEASURED FROM POINT WHERE THE DOOR HITS THE WALL.

MAX. 6 FT. (1.8 m)

MAX. 12 FT. (3.6 m)

MAX. 6 FT. (1.8 m)

BASEBOARD HEATER

FIRE PLACE

LOCATE OUTLETS AT ENDS OF BASEBOARD HEATERS SO THAT APPLIANCE SUPPLY CORDS NEED NOT PASS OVER HEATER. (AND BE ROASTED DAILY)

ANY WALL SPACE WHICH IS 39 IN. (1 m) OR MORE IN LENGTH MUST HAVE ONE OR MORE OUTLETS.

— **Electric Baseboard Heaters** — are a permanent unit and they do limit the use of that wall space to some extent, however, appliances such as radios, T.V., swag lamps, etc. can be placed in that wall space. The rule therefore, does require outlets in wall spaces occupied by electric baseboard heaters. These outlets **should not be located above the heaters** unless it cannot be avoided. Usually they can be located at the ends of the heaters so that electrical supply cords need not run over the heater and be roasted every time the heater comes on. See also Appendix B on page 460 in the Electrical Code for confirmation of this recommendation.

(iii) **Entrance (Foyer)** — Rule 26-702(6) - if this is a room, treat it as a living room. If it is like a hallway, apply the rule for hallways. If it is something in between — well — just put in the extra outlets and be done with it — don't quibble over little things.

(iv) **Hallway**— Rule 26-702(6) — The hallway requires at least one **duplex** plug outlet for every 4.5 m(approx. 15 ft.) measured along the center line. Remember, this applies to each hallway separately.

Note — A short open—type hallway (such as between a living room and kitchen where there are **no doors**) does not require a plug outlet at all, provided that no point in the hallway is more than 4.5 m(approx. 15 ft.) from a plug outlet in either of the rooms at the ends of the hallway.

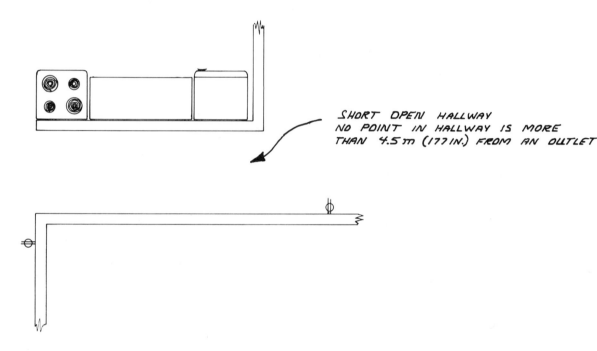

SHORT OPEN HALLWAY
NO POINT IN HALLWAY IS MORE
THAN 4.5m (177 IN.) FROM AN OUTLET

(v) **Basement Wiring** — Rule 26-702

Finished Basement — The rules require the same number of outlets along the walls of a basement as for similar rooms upstairs. Basement bedrooms, hallways, family rooms etc. which are finished must be wired as similar rooms on the main floor.

Unfinished Basement - Rule 26-702(2) & (7)

First A Definition of Unfinished — Bulletin 26-2-0(3)

This bulletin defines an unfinished basement as follows:

(a)   if the wall finish material does not extend fully to the floor, ie. if the lower 15¾ in. of the wall is not finished with any kind of finishing material that wall is considered to be unfinished. Such a wall is required to have only minimum wiring as described below. Building Insulation and vapour barrier may be installed in all walls and it may extend to the floor. Building insulation is not finishing material.

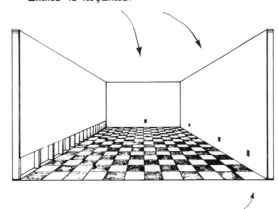

THESE WALLS ARE FINISHED THEREFORE FULL WIRING IS REQUIRED.

OPEN - NOT FINISHED WALL. THE BULLETIN SAYS THIS IS AN UNFINISHED WALL. BECAUSE THE LOWER 15¾ IN. IS OPEN.

NO PLUG OUTLETS REQUIRED ON THIS WALL BECAUSE THIS FLOOR AREA ALREADY HAS PLUG OUTLETS ON THE OTHER WALLS.

THIS WALL IS FINISHED THEREFORE FULL WIRING IS REQUIRED.

(b) each wall or partition is considered separately. Full wiring is required in all walls and partitions which are finished completely. If only the outside walls of the basement are finished to the floor then only those walls require full wiring as similar rooms on the main floor. Any wall of any basement room where the wall finish stops 15¾ in. above the floor need not be wired except as noted below under Minimum Basement Plug OutletsRequired.

Minimum Basement Plug Outlets Required - Rule 26-702(7)(c) - requires at least one plug outlet in an unfinished basement. If there are no walls to divide the basement into two or more **areas** the rule is satisfied with just one duplex plug outlet in the whole basement. If the laundry facilities are in the basement the washing machine will require another separate plug outlet on a separate circuit as noted below.

Basement Partitions - unfinished -(studs only)

If there are no partitions to divide the basement into two or more areas **AND** the lower portion of the outside basement walls are not finished except as described above, **AND** there is no laundry facility in the basement, this rule is satisfied with just one duplex plug outlet in the whole basement.

Caution: - Note that Rule 26-702(7)(c) refers to "area". The rule says "At least one duplex receptacle shall be provided in any unfinished basement area". This means that unfinished partitions, studs only, will divide the basement into two or more areas each requiring a plug outlet. The rule can be correctly interpreted to say that if there are unfinished partitions, even if they consist of studs only, which divide the basement into two or more areas, the rule could be said to require an outlet in each such area created by these unfinished partitions. Check this point with your Inspector.

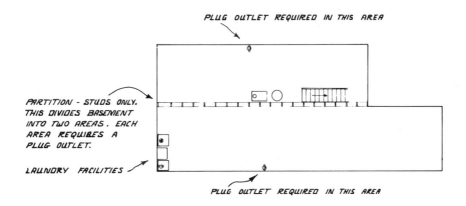

PLUG OUTLET REQUIRED IN THIS AREA

PARTITION - STUDS ONLY. THIS DIVIDES BASEMENT INTO TWO AREAS. EACH AREA REQUIRES A PLUG OUTLET.

LAUNDRY FACILITIES

PLUG OUTLET REQUIRED IN THIS AREA

Laundry Plug in Basement. If laundry facilities are located in the basement the plug outlet for the washer is **in addition to** the minimum plug outlets described above and it must be on it's own circuit.

FRIDGE – DUPLEX RECEPTACLE ON SEPARATE CIRCUIT IS REQUIRED.

COUNTER OUTLETS – NO POINT ALONG BACK EDGE OF COUNTER MAY BE MORE THAN 900 mm (35.5 IN) FROM AN OUTLET.

- 300 mm 11.8 IN OR LONGER COUNTER SPACE REQUIRES A PLUG OUTLET.

- ADJACENT OUTLETS MAY NOT BE ON SAME CIRCUIT.

DINING AREA IN KITCHEN – ONE OR MORE PLUG OUTLETS REQUIRED HERE – TREAT AS LIVING ROOM OUTLETS MAY BE SUPPLIED WITH LIGHTING CIRCUIT.

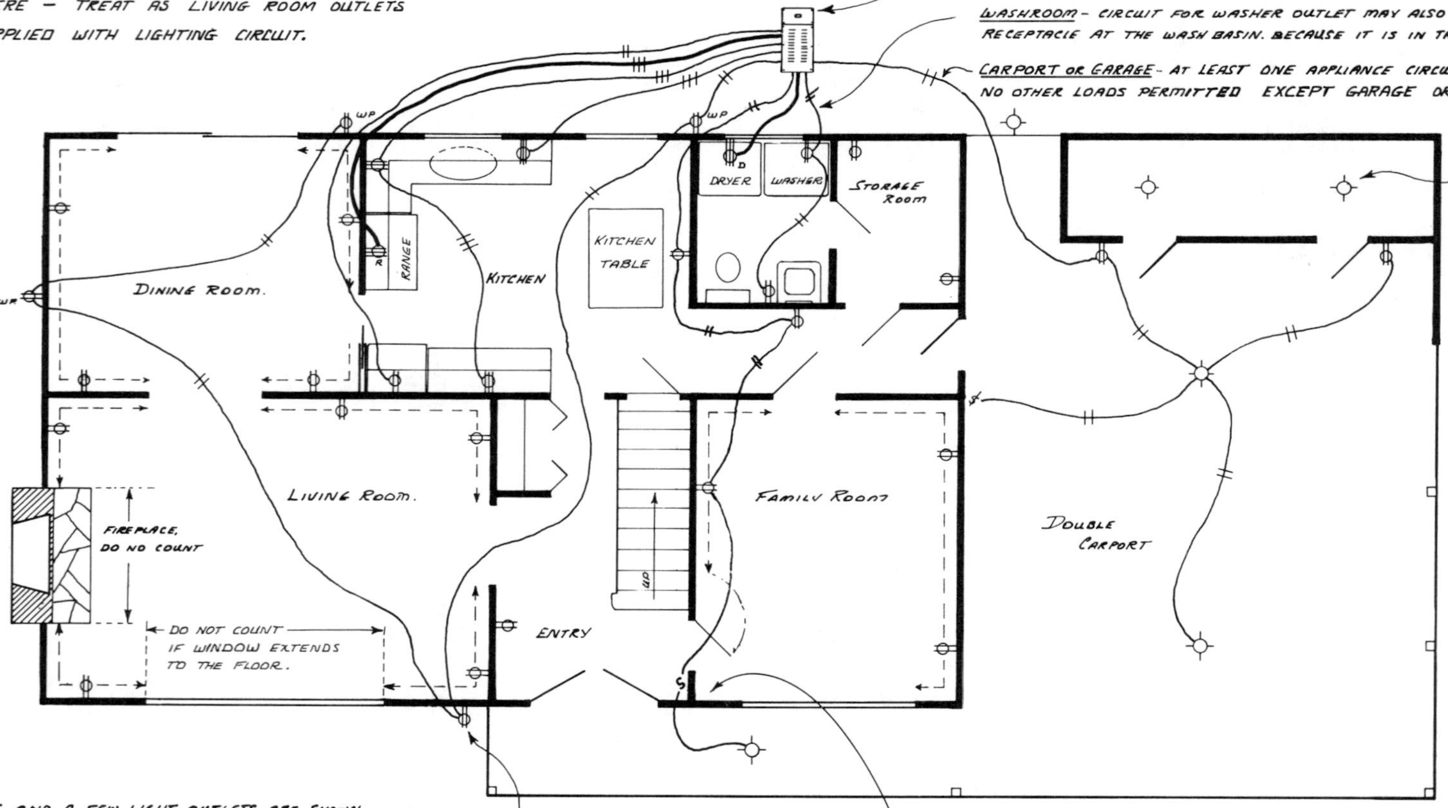

NOTES.

- ONLY PLUG OUTLETS AND A FEW LIGHT OUTLETS ARE SHOWN.

- BEDROOMS ARE NOT SHOWN – PLUG OUTLETS IN THESE ROOMS ARE SPACED AS IN THE LIVING ROOM OR FAMILY ROOM.

- BASEMENT WIRING NOT SHOWN.

SEE SECTION ON SERVICES FOR MORE DETAIL.

WASHROOM - CIRCUIT FOR WASHER OUTLET MAY ALSO SUPPLY THE RECEPTACLE AT THE WASH BASIN. BECAUSE IT IS IN THE LAUNDRY ROOM.

CARPORT OR GARAGE - AT LEAST ONE APPLIANCE CIRCUIT IS REQUIRED. NO OTHER LOADS PERMITTED EXCEPT GARAGE OR CARPORT LIGHTS.

STORAGE ROOM & OUTDOOR LIGHTING MAY NOT BE ON CAR-PORT OR GARAGE PLUG OUTLET CIRCUIT.

ANY WALL SPACE 900 mm (35.5 IN) OR MORE IN WIDTH MUST HAVE A PLUG OUTLET

NOTE – THIS SHORT SPACE REQUIRES A PLUG OUTLET. THE LONGEST WALL LENGTH IS ONLY 600 mm 24 IN BUT MEASURED INTO THE CORNER, AS REQUIRED BY RULE 26-702 (2), THE LENGTH IS 1140 mm (45 IN.)

OUTDOOR RECEPTACLES

- SEPARATE CIRCUIT IS REQUIRED.
- MAX. 12 OUTLETS PER CIRCUIT.
- DUPLEX TYPE REQUIRED.
- G.F.C.I TYPE CIRCUIT BREAKER OR RECEPTACLE MUST BE USED.

DOUBLE CARPORT

STORAGE ROOM

FAMILY ROOM

UP / DN

KITCHEN TABLE

KITCHEN

RANGE

WASHER / DRYER

DINING ROOM

LIVING ROOM

ENTRY

FIREPLACE, DO NO COUNT

DO NOT COUNT IF WINDOW EXTENDS TO THE FLOOR.

(j) <u>**Bathroom Plug Outlet**</u> – Rule 26-702(8)(9)(10) requires at least 1 plug outlet in each bathroom.

This outlet must:

— be at least 1 m(39 in.) away from the bathtub or shower stall. Things have changed. This is now a **horizontal** distance as shown below.

— be adjacent to the wash basin. The rule requires that this outlet be not above the basin but on either side of it.

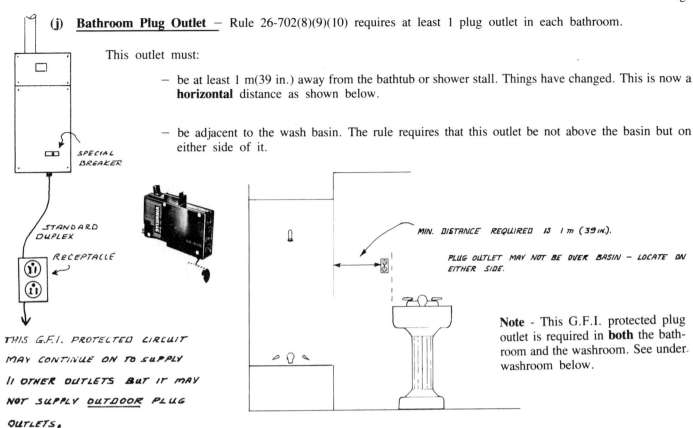

SPECIAL BREAKER

STANDARD DUPLEX

RECEPTACLE

THIS G.F.I. PROTECTED CIRCUIT MAY CONTINUE ON TO SUPPLY II OTHER OUTLETS BUT IT MAY NOT SUPPLY OUTDOOR PLUG OUTLETS.

MIN. DISTANCE REQUIRED IS 1 m (39 IN.).

PLUG OUTLET MAY NOT BE OVER BASIN – LOCATE ON EITHER SIDE.

Note - This G.F.I. protected plug outlet is required in **both** the bathroom and the washroom. See under washroom below.

— be either GFI type **receptacle**; or

may be an ordinary duplex plug receptacle which is supplied from a special type circuit breaker (G.F.C.I.) in the service panel. This circuit breaker is called Class A ground fault interrupter. These breakers mount in the service panel as ordinary breakers. If you are using an older type circuit breaker panel make sure they are available for the particular service panel you are using.

— **not** be a transformer type plug outlet especially designed for electric razors. These are no longer acceptable. The rules now require GFI protected receptacles.

Note – Rule 26-704(7) was **not amended** this time. This means we may **not** supply the bathroom plug outlet with the same circuit which supplies the outdoor plug outlets. The bathroom plug outlet may be supplied with any lighting circuit which has eleven or less outlets.

Note - Bathroom/Laundry Room Combination – Rule 26-702(11) – This is an important detail. See under 'Laundry in Bathroom', page 65.

(k) <u>**Washroom Plug Outlet**</u> - Rule 26-702(1)

This rule says "a washroom means a room containing a wash basin but without bathing or showering facilities".

(i) **Plug outlet Required** - Rule 26-702(9) requires at least one duplex plug outlet adjacent, ie. next to but not above, the wash basin.

(ii) **Circuit Required** - The rules do not require a separate circuit. This outlet may be connected to any nearby lighting circuit.

(iii) **G.F.I. protection Required** - Rule 26-702(9) - Yes, this outlet must be G.F.I. protected. You may connect the G.F.I. receptacle in the **bathroom** so that it will also protect this washroom plug outlet. Follow the wiring diagram on the instruction sheet that comes with the G.F.I. receptacle.

(l) <u>**Other Rooms or Areas**</u>

(i) **Storage Rooms** – Rule 26-702(2) – Every **finished** room, including storage rooms, must have minimum wiring so that no point along the wall is more than 1.8 m(71 in.) from a plug receptacle.

Note — Storage spaces such as areas under the stairways, attics or crawl spaces do not require a plug outlet. In fact it is safer without one, so that appliances must be unplugged before being stored away.

(ii) **Closets, Cupboards, Cabinets etc.** — Rule 26-702(12) prohibits plug outlets in these enclosures except for special cavities built for specific non−heating appliances such as radios or T.V. sets.

(iii) **Dining Room** — Rule 26-702(5)(c) - Dining rooms which are **not part of a kitchen** must be wired as a living room so that no part along the wall is more than 1.8 m(71 in.) from a plug outlet, rule 26-702(1). For dining or eating areas forming part of a kitchen, see under 'Appliance Outlets' below.

(j) **Kitchen Appliance Plug Outlets**

(i) **Types Permitted** — Rule 26-702(16)

Duplex Receptacle — all appliance outlets must be duplex type. The single receptacle may be used in only a few special cases.

SPLIT Duplex Receptacles — **must be used** for **all** kitchen **counter** plug receptacles. Single receptacles **may not** be used in these locations.

This is a standard duplex receptacle, except that it has a small break−away section of metal on the hot (brass coloured) side terminal block as shown at left. When this section of metal is broken off it disconnects the two halves of the duplex receptacle from each other so that each half can be connected to a different circuit. They share a common neutral (white) wire. Two such split duplex receptacles may be connected to a 3−wire circuit as shown below.

These **must be used** for all appliance outlets above the **counter** work space in the kitchen. Remember, that half of **each** duplex receptacle is one one circuit and the **other two halves** are on the other circuit of a 3−wire circuit − see diagram. This arrangement is intended to prevent nuisance tripping of the circuit breaker when two appliances are plugged in at the same time.

It has been determined, we are not told how, that the average homemaker in an average home is much more likely to use two adjacent receptacles at the same time than two spaced a bit farther apart. In the authors opinion this requirement is confusing to the homeowner and of little practical help to anyone. Some provinces have amended this rule to require a separate 3−wire circuit to each duplex outlet along the kitchen counter work area. The cost is a little higher, however, the result is no confusion and no nuisance tripping of circuit breakers and that's got to be a big plus. However, we are stuck with the rule as described above and as the man said, "Ours is not to reason why but to do or ...... whatever".

NOTE — BREAKERS ARE SIDE BY SIDE AND TIE-BARS ARE REQUIRED RULE 14-302 (6)

3 WIRE LOOMEX

RED WIRE
BLACK WIRE

ADJACENT OUTLETS MUST BE ON DIFFERENT CIRCUITS.

NOTE — REMOVE THE SMALL BREAK AWAY SECTION OF METAL BETWEEN THE BRASS SCREWS ON EACH SPLIT DUPLEX RECEPTACLE.

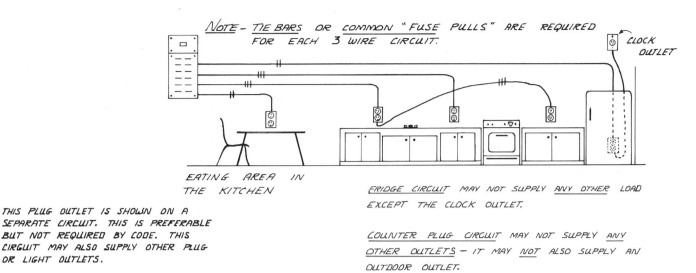

NOTE - TIE BARS OR COMMON "FUSE PULLS" ARE REQUIRED FOR EACH 3 WIRE CIRCUIT.

CLOCK OUTLET

EATING AREA IN THE KITCHEN

THIS PLUG OUTLET IS SHOWN ON A SEPARATE CIRCUIT. THIS IS PREFERABLE BUT NOT REQUIRED BY CODE. THIS CIRCUIT MAY ALSO SUPPLY OTHER PLUG OR LIGHT OUTLETS.

FRIDGE CIRCUIT MAY NOT SUPPLY ANY OTHER LOAD EXCEPT THE CLOCK OUTLET.

COUNTER PLUG CIRCUIT MAY NOT SUPPLY ANY OTHER OUTLETS — IT MAY NOT ALSO SUPPLY AN OUTDOOR OUTLET.

Notes:

(1) As shown above, the two split duplex receptacles to the left of the range are on different **3−wire circuits**. The outlet on each side of the range are also on different **3−wire circuits**. This is to comply with Rule 26-704(3)(c) which says that "adjacent receptacles shall not be connected to the same 3-wire circuit".

(2) Where breakers are used to supply split receptacles, tie−bars must be installed on the handles so they operate as one breaker. Rules 14-010, 14-302(b).

Where fuses are used rule 14-010 requires that both fuses can be removed simultaneously. A "fuse pull" similar to that required for a range or dryer, is used. Where the fuse panel being used is not equipped with this feature, check with your Inspector for permission to install separate disconnect for these circuits.

(3) **Polarization** − This is an important detail. You will notice the receptacle has a brass terminal screw and the chrome plated terminal screw. Be sure to connect the black, or sometimes the red wire, to the brass terminal screw and the white neutral conductor to the chrome plated terminal screw. The Inspector has a little tester he uses to check this connection without removing any cover etc. If you have connected incorrectly, he will find it.

(ii) **Kitchen** − According to rule 26-702(5) appliance outlets are required as follows:

Fridge Outlet

A **duplex** receptacle must be installed for each fridge. It may **not** be a **single** receptacle. It could be a split duplex receptacle but then **both** circuits of the 3−wire supply circuit would have to end there. One of these circuits would never be used because the receptacle is usually behind the fridge and not readily accessible for other loads.

Note − The circuit supplying a fridge outlet **may not** continue on to supply any other load except a clock outlet. Rule 26-704(2).

Counter Outlets

A sufficient number of receptacles must be installed so that no point along the wall line on the work surface will be more than 900 mm(35.4 in.) from a receptacle. This is measured from the receptacle along the **back edge** of the counter, as shown.

Work Surface does not include area of sink, range, fridge or similar appliance.

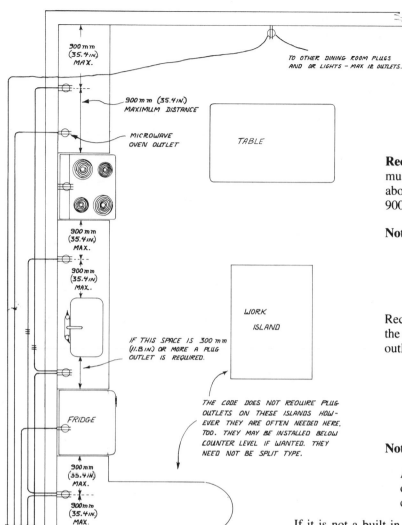

300 mm
(35.4 IN.)
MAX.

900 mm (35.4 IN.)
MAXIMUM DISTANCE

MICROWAVE
OVEN OUTLET

TO OTHER DINING ROOM PLUGS
AND OR LIGHTS - MAX 12 OUTLETS.

TABLE

900 mm
(35.4 IN.)
MAX.

900 mm
(35.4 IN.)
MAX.

IF THIS SPACE IS 300 mm
(11.8 IN.) OR MORE A PLUG
OUTLET IS REQUIRED.

WORK
ISLAND

THE CODE DOES NOT REQUIRE PLUG
OUTLETS ON THESE ISLANDS HOW-
EVER THEY ARE OFTEN NEEDED HERE,
TOO. THEY MAY BE INSTALLED BELOW
COUNTER LEVEL IF WANTED. THEY
NEED NOT BE SPLIT TYPE.

FRIDGE

900 mm
(35.4 IN.)
MAX.

900 mm
(35.4 IN.)
MAX.

Eating Area in Kitchen - Rule 26-702(5)(c)

Treat this eating area as you would any other wall space in the living room or bedroom. No point along the floor line of the wall may be more than 1.8 m(71 in.) from a plug outlet. The plug outlets in this space need not be on a separate circuit. They may be supplied with any lighting circuit.

Receptacles Required — Each of these work surfaces must have a plug receptacle. No point along the wall line above the work counter may be more than 900 mm(approx. 36 in.) from a plug receptacle.

Note — Any counter space which is 300 mm(approx. 12 in.) long must be provided with one or more outlets. Any counter space **less** than 300 mm(approx. 12 in.) long is not required to have an outlet.

Receptacle on Range — Rule 26-702(17) - Plug outlets on the range are **not acceptable** as alternatives for wall outlets.

Note 1 - Built-in Microwave Oven - Rule 26-704(9)

A separate circuit is required for a **built-in** microwave oven. The plug outlet must be located in the special cavity built for this oven.

If it is not a built-in oven, i.e., if it stands on the kitchen counter, the rule does not apply. In that case one of the counter outlets may be used to supply the oven.

Note 2 — Work Surface - Rule 26-702(5)

As shown, the counter work space is often divided into several isolated sections. Each of these isolated sections must be considered separately and each must have a split duplex receptacle if it is 300 mm(11.8 in.) or longer. This measurement is along the **back wall** of the counter space. The reason for this requirement is to make all counter work surfaces properly accessible to appliance receptacles without the supply lines having to cross over sinks, ranges, etc.. Make sure you have a sufficient number of outlets along the counter before covering. It is difficult to add more later after the finish material is in place.

Note 3 — Work Island - Rule 26-702(5)

This is not a problem area. It need not be considered as far as the 900 mm(35.4 in.) distance rule is concerned. An appliance outlet located on the wall at the back of the island, as shown, is considered sufficient for the island.

Note 4 — Appliance Storage Garage - Rule 26-702(12)

Some modern kitchen cabinets provide space inside the cabinets to store the appliances normally left standing on the kitchen counter. There is nothing wrong with this provided the appliances **cannot be left plugged in** when they are stored in that cavity. The plug outlets may **not** be inside that enclosure.

Split Duplex Receptacles — Rule 26-702(5)(b) all receptacles along counter work surfaces **must be split duplex type.**

— Single receptacle may **not** be used.
— Only two such split duplex receptacles may be supplied from a 3—wire circuit.
— This 3—wire circuit may not supply any other load.

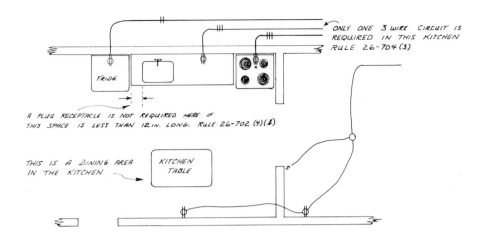

— Adjacent receptacles may not be served with the same 3—wire circuit. Wherever two or more counter outlets are required because of counter length, 2 or more 3—wire circuits are required to supply these outlets.

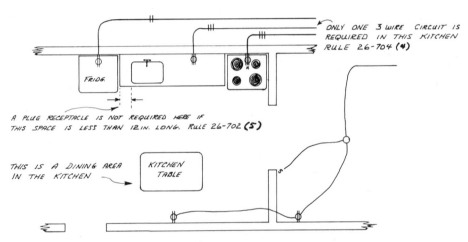

(iii)   **Dining Areas**

Kitchen Dining Area — Rule 26-702(5)(c)

Eating areas in the kitchen must be treated as any other room such as living room or bedroom. Plug outlets are required so that no point along the floor line of the wall is more than 1.8 m(71 in.) distance from a plug outlet. One or more outlets may be required. All these plug outlets may be supplied from any lighting circuit — total must not exceed 12 outlets per circuit.

Dining Room — Rule 26-702(2)

A dining room which is a **separate** room and not part of the kitchen must be wired similar to the living room, i.e. no point along the floor line of the walls may be more than 1.8 m(71 in.) from a plug outlet. These outlets **are not** required to be on appliance circuits. They may be supplied with any lighting circuit.

(iv)   **Laundry Room or Area** — Rules 26-702(7)(a), 26-704(6)

At least one appliance plug outlet must be installed in the laundry room or area.

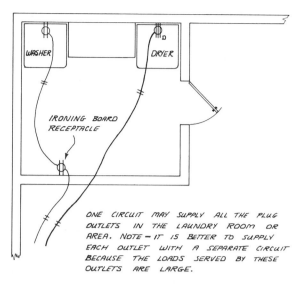

This outlet:

- must be **duplex** type — a single receptacle is not acceptable in the laundry room. It may be, but does not need to be, a split receptacle.

- may be at any convenient height in the laundry room.

- must be supplied by a circuit used for no other purpose than to supply the one or more duplex appliance plug receptacles in the laundry room or area.

Note — The rule says we must provide "at least one branch circuit ..... for receptacles" in the laundry room. According to this rule, two or more receptacles in the laundry area could be supplied by one circuit. It is better to install more circuits — one for each outlet. If there is sufficient space to do the ironing in this room you should, not must, install a separate circuit for the iron.

ONE CIRCUIT MAY SUPPLY ALL THE PLUG OUTLETS IN THE LAUNDRY ROOM OR AREA. NOTE — IT IS BETTER TO SUPPLY EACH OUTLET WITH A SEPARATE CIRCUIT BECAUSE THE LOADS SERVED BY THESE OUTLETS ARE LARGE.

(v)   **Utility Room or Area** — Rules 26-702(7)(b), 26-704(6)

These rules require at least one duplex plug outlet in "each utility room". The term "utility room" is not defined in the code. It is not refering to the laundry room because that room or area is dealt with separately under another subrule. It could be the furnace and water heater room but then what on earth would we do with a plug outlet in that room. It would serve no obvious purpose there.

Since there is no definition of this term "utility room" then obviously no one can be sure when he is in that room. Rooms like that are difficult to wire properly. (It would be just as difficult to prove it was not wired properly.)

It is possible this rule was intended to address what is sometimes called a mud room, ie, the first room one would enter with dirty boots. The freezer is often located in this room. The rule therefore correctly requires at least one plug outlet (more than one may be needed) for cleaning purposes and to supply any appliances which may be located in this room.

(vi)   **Laundry in Bathroom** — Rule 26-702(11)

There are some very important details to remember when locating laundry equipment in a bathroom. These are major changes from the last code.

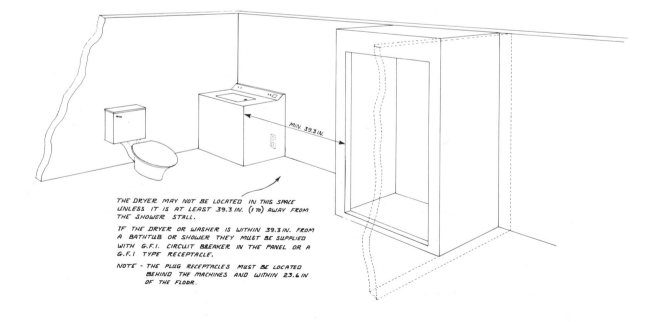

THE DRYER MAY NOT BE LOCATED IN THIS SPACE UNLESS IT IS AT LEAST 39.3 IN. (1 m) AWAY FROM THE SHOWER STALL.

IF THE DRYER OR WASHER IS WITHIN 39.3 IN. FROM A BATHTUB OR SHOWER THEY MUST BE SUPPLIED WITH G.F.I. CIRCUIT BREAKER IN THE PANEL OR A G.F.I TYPE RECEPTACLE.

NOTE — THE PLUG RECEPTACLES MUST BE LOCATED BEHIND THE MACHINES AND WITHIN 23.6 IN OF THE FLOOR.

MIN. 39.3 IN.

(1) Locate the washer plug outlet **behind** the washer.

(2) Locate the dryer plug outlet **behind** the dryer.

(3) Both outlets **must not** be more than 23.6 in. (600 m) above the floor.

The reason for these first three requirements is to make the outlets inaccessible for use with any other electrical appliances.

(4) **Out of Reach requirement** - Both dryer and washer must be at least 39.3 in. (1 m) away from the bathtub or shower stall.

CAUTION   - If any **one** of the above requirements is not complied with the rule requires GFI protection for **both** dryer and washer.

One quick check on the price of a 2-pole 30 amp GFI circuit breaker will make it a lot easier to decide how to do this installation. Those breakers are expensive. It may be less expensive to increase the size of the room to provide the necessary clearances or to locate the laundry equipment eleswhere in another room.

(vii) **Dryer Receptacles** – see under "Heavy Appliances", page 86.

(viii) **Freezer Outlet**

The rules do not demand a separate circuit for the freezer but it is a good idea. We are still allowed to think of this one ourselves. The possible loss of a freezer full of meat because someone tripped the circuit and forgot to reset it, makes this a good investment.

(ix) **Outdoor Outlets** – Rules 26-702(13) & (14), 26-704(7) & Bulletin 26-2-0(6)(7)(8)

Basic requirement - Rule 26-702(13) - The rules require at least one plug outlet which is "readily accessible from ground or grade level for the use of appliances which, of necessity, are used outdoors."

These outlets must:

- be duplex type - single outlet is not acceptable.

- be readily accessible, which means it must not be necessary to use chairs or ladders to reach the plug outlet. See definition on page 41 of the code.

- be supplied with a circuit used solely for this one or more **outdoor plug outlets.**

- be supplied with a Class A ground fault circuit interrupter.

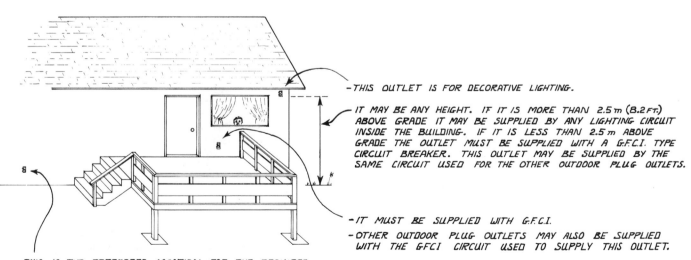

-THIS OUTLET IS FOR DECORATIVE LIGHTING.

- IT MAY BE ANY HEIGHT. IF IT IS MORE THAN 2.5 m (8.2 FT.) ABOVE GRADE IT MAY BE SUPPLIED BY ANY LIGHTING CIRCUIT INSIDE THE BUILDING. IF IT IS LESS THAN 2.5 m ABOVE GRADE THE OUTLET MUST BE SUPPLIED WITH A G.F.C.I. TYPE CIRCUIT BREAKER. THIS OUTLET MAY BE SUPPLIED BY THE SAME CIRCUIT USED FOR THE OTHER OUTDOOR PLUG OUTLETS.

-IT MUST BE SUPPLIED WITH G.F.C.I.
- OTHER OUTDOOR PLUG OUTLETS MAY ALSO BE SUPPLIED WITH THE GFCI CIRCUIT USED TO SUPPLY THIS OUTLET.

- THIS IS THE PREFERRED LOCATION FOR THE REQUIRED OUTDOOR PLUG OUTLET.
- IT MUST BE SUPPLIED WITH GFCI TYPE CIRCUIT BKR.
- OTHER OUTDOOR PLUG OUTLETS MAY ALSO BE SUPPLIED FROM THIS CIRCUIT BREAKER.

NOTES and BEWARES.

(1) **Sundeck Plug Outlets** - If the deck is low and the plug outlets are within 8.2 ft. of ground or grade level the plug outlets must be G.F.I. protected with either a circuit breaker in the panel or a G.F.I. type receptacle. These outlets must be supplied with a separate circuit used for no other purpose or with the circuit which supplies the other outdoor outlets.

(2) **Higher Sundecks** - Where the outlet on the sundeck is more than 8.2 ft. (2.5 m) above ground or grade level it may still be supplied with the same G.F.I. circuit breaker as noted above but it **is not required** to be on this circuit. It could be supplied with any nearby lighting circuit.

(3) **Other Outdoor Plugs** - Bulletin 26-2-0(8) - The above requirements apply to **all outdoor** plug outlets including those located in a flower garden for special lighting and plugs located on other out buildings such as a separate garage. Whenever these outlets are within 8.2 ft. of ground or grade level they must be G.F.I. protected as described above.

(4) **Bathroom Plugs** - Rule 26-704(7) was not revised in this code. This means that we now need separate G.F.I. protection for the bathroom plug outlet. Separate G.F.I. protection for the outdoor plugs and yes we will need a separate circuit and G.F.I. protection for the carport plug outlet. Things do get complicated don't they.

(5) **Decorative Lighting Outlets (Christmas Lighting)** - These plug outlets need not be G.F.I. protected if they are 8.2 ft. (2.5 m) above ground or grade level. If they are 8.2 ft. or less above grade level they must be wired as described for any other outdoor plug outlet.

(6) **Two Wire Cable** - Use only 2-wire cable for this circuit. The G.F.I. will not work if wired with 3-wire cable.

(7) **Maximum Circuit Load** - The rule requires at least one circuit for outdoor plug outlets. Where there are two or more outdoor plug outlets these may all be supplied with one circuit provided the number of outlets does not exceed 12.

WHAT'S A G.F.C.I. FOR?   WHAT'S IT DO?.......it saves lives.

When an electrical appliance is faulty the appliance itself may become energized. Anyone holding such an appliance could become part of that supply circuit. He would become an electrical conductor. The current would flow through the person to ground. Only a very small current is needed to kill a human being. The graph indicates the enormous difference between the small amount needed to kill a person and the large amount available in every 15 amp. circuit in the house.

It would be very expensive to protect all the circuits in the house with these special circuit breakers. What's more, it is not necessary. The code requires only certain outlets to be protected with this special breaker. As indicated above, outdoor plug outlets are among those outlets which must be protected with this special circuit breaker.

15 AMPS.

50 m a   FIBRILLATION & DEATH

18 m a   RESPIRATION AFFECTED

6-9 m a   LET-GO THRESHOLD
3-5 m a   G.F.C.I. BREAKER TRIPPING RANGE.
1 m a   PERCEPTION

QWIK-GARD
CIRCUIT BREAKER

The graph also indicates the very low current that a G.F.C.I. will pass to ground. It is designed to trip at a maximum 5 m.a. This means that a person holding a faulty electrical appliance, such as an electric lawnmower or an electric drill, could get an electrical shock but the circuit breaker would open the circuit before the current reached a dangerous level.

(ix) **Carport only Plug Outlets** − Rules 26-702(15), 26-704(8)

At least one appliance plug outlet must be installed for each car space in the carport or garage.

This outlet must:
- be **duplex** type − single outlet is not acceptable.
- be installed, one in **each** car space. (The rule does not say 'in' each car space it says 'for' each car space. However, the intent of the rule seems to be that there should be a plug outlet **in** each car space.)
- be supplied with a circuit used solely for these outlets located in a carport except that the carport lighting may also be supplied with this circuit.

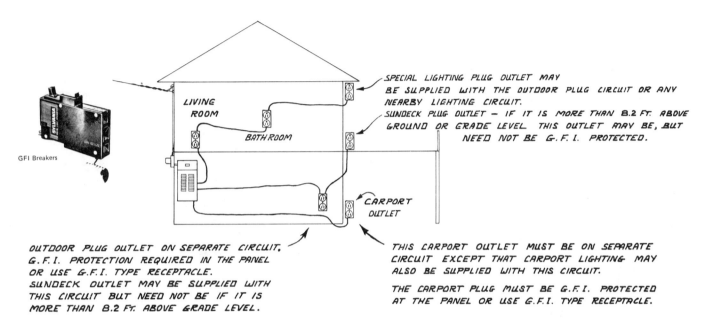

GFI Breakers

SPECIAL LIGHTING PLUG OUTLET MAY BE SUPPLIED WITH THE OUTDOOR PLUG CIRCUIT OR ANY NEARBY LIGHTING CIRCUIT.

SUNDECK PLUG OUTLET − IF IT IS MORE THAN 8.2 FT. ABOVE GROUND OR GRADE LEVEL THIS OUTLET MAY BE, BUT NEED NOT BE G.F.I. PROTECTED.

LIVING ROOM

BATHROOM

CARPORT OUTLET

OUTDOOR PLUG OUTLET ON SEPARATE CIRCUIT. G.F.I. PROTECTION REQUIRED IN THE PANEL OR USE G.F.I. TYPE RECEPTACLE. SUNDECK OUTLET MAY BE SUPPLIED WITH THIS CIRCUIT BUT NEED NOT BE IF IT IS MORE THAN 8.2 FT. ABOVE GRADE LEVEL.

THIS CARPORT OUTLET MUST BE ON SEPARATE CIRCUIT EXCEPT THAT CARPORT LIGHTING MAY ALSO BE SUPPLIED WITH THIS CIRCUIT.

THE CARPORT PLUG MUST BE G.F.I. PROTECTED AT THE PANEL OR USE G.F.I. TYPE RECEPTACLE.

Notes

(1) **Definition** - Bulletin 26-2-0(7) says that a carport plug outlet is now considered to be an outdoor plug outlet. This is an important definition and it is long overdue.

(2) **G.F.I. Protection Required** - Rule 26-702(14) says all outdoor plug outlets within 8.2 ft. of ground or grade level must be protected with a G.F.I. circuit breaker in the panel or with a G.F.I. type plug receptacle.

(3) **Separate Circuit Required** - Rule 26-704(8) says the circuit used to supply these carport outlets must be a separate circuit used for no other loads. This means that even though this carport plug outlet is called an outdoor plug outlet it may **not** be supplied with the circuit used for the other outdoor plug outlets, a separate circuit is required.

(4) **Bathroom Plugs** - Rule 26-704(7) was **not** revised in new code. This means that the bathroom plugs may **not** be supplied with this carport plug circuit.

(x) **Garage Plug Outlets** - Rules 26-702(15) & 26-704(8)

At least appliance plug outlet must be installed in each car space in a garage.

This outlet must:

- be duplex type - single receptacle is not acceptable.
- be installed so that there is a plug outlet for each car space.
- be supplied with a circuit used solely for these outlets located in the garage except that lighting fixtures and garage door openers may also be connected to this circuit.

Note **G.F.I. protection** - The garage plug outlets are not required to be protected with a G.F.I. type circuit breaker.

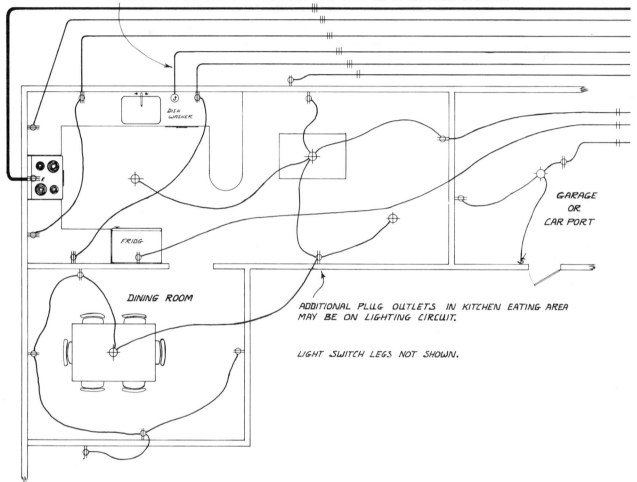

3 WIRE FOR DISHWASHER & GARBAGE DISPOSER MAY BE RUN INTO JUNCTION
BOX THEN 2 WIRE CABLES TO LOADS. NOTE JB MUST BE IN ACCESSIBLE LOCATION.

DISH WASHER

FRIDG

DINING ROOM

GARAGE OR CAR PORT

ADDITIONAL PLUG OUTLETS IN KITCHEN EATING AREA MAY BE ON LIGHTING CIRCUIT.

LIGHT SWITCH LEGS NOT SHOWN.

(k) **Junction Boxes**

(i) **Accessibility** − Rules 12-3018(1), 12-112(3) − They must remain accessible. This means they may not be hidden inside a wall or ceiling or similar place.

(ii) **Head Clearance** − Rule 12-3018(2) − Where junction boxes are installed in an attic or crawl space, there shall be at least 900 mm(35.4 in.) vertical space to provide access.

(iii) **Where To Use** − Use junction boxes very sparingly, only where you absolutely have to. Usually all your joints are made up in light, switch or plug outlet boxes.

(l) **Door Bell Transformer** − Rule 16-200, 16-204

(i) **Type** - must be a CSA certified Class II transformer. This is usually die−stamped somewhere on the transformer. This Class II label is very important. It means the transformer is designed so that it will not be a fire hazard even if improperly wired.

(ii) **Circuit** − may be connected to any lighting circuit.

(iii) **Location** − Watch this one. This transformer must be located somewhere where it will remain accessible. This means it may not be inside a finished wall or ceiling where there is no access.

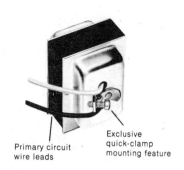

Primary circuit
wire leads

Exclusive
quick-clamp
mounting feature

Do not mount it inside the service panel. It may be nippled into the side of the branch circuit panel provided the wall finish is kept back to keep it exposed and accessible.

The furnace room or basement workshop area is usually a good location for this transformer.

(iv) **Cable** − Type LVT cable may be used.

13.   TYPE OF BOXES

(a) **Type -** There are many types of boxes available but only a few are in common use today.

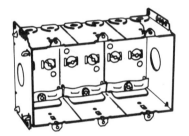

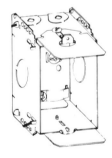

(i)   **Internal Cable Clamps**

Use the clamp properly. Where the cable enters the back or top knockout, as shown, it must emerge at the lower edge. It is not correct to double it back over the sharp edge, as shown.

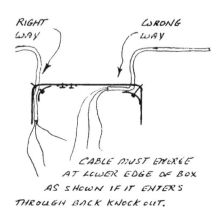

(ii)   **Saucer Boxes** − The restrictions on the use of this box have been removed. This box may be used anywhere that similar deeper boxes are permitted.

Caution - do not use the center KO hole in this box unless the fixture you plan to connect to this outlet is the simple lampholder type shown.

Most light fixtures use a mounting strap to hold the fixture in place. There is usually a long hollow bolt which runs through the center of the fixture base and into the mounting strap. It's this long hollow bolt that may cause trouble if it extends too far into the shallow box because it is directly in line with the center KO hole in the box. If your supply cable enters the center KO hole it could be seriously damaged with this fixture mounting bolt. For this reason you should **never enter a shallow box through the center KO hole**. Always use one of the off center KO holes for cable entry. That center KO was not intended for cable entry but for special box mounting and heavy fixture support with a special box supporting bar.

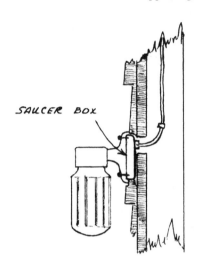

SAUCER BOX

These shallow boxes are often used at front and back doors when the outside wall finish is not smooth. As shown, the box is fastened directly to the outside rough sheathing. Because it is so shallow it need not be recessed into the sheathing. When the finish siding is installed the box may be shifted to match the boards so that it is fully recessed into the **outer** finish sheathing material. This eliminates the possibility of the outlet box being somewhere on the joint, between two boards, where it is difficult to fit the fixture properly.

Note - Box Loading - saucer boxes are very shallow, approximatelt ½ in. deep, and therefoe may be used only at the end of a cable run. Only one 2-conductor #14 or #12 cable may enter this box. This means that you must run to the switch box first then to this light outlet box.

(b)   <u>**Box Support**</u> − Rules 12-3014, 12-3016, 12-3022

(i)   **Nail−on Type** − These are the most practical, they are available in plastic or metal. Note the large ears for fastening. They may be nailed on. If nails are used they should be driven all the way in − not just halfway, then bent over.

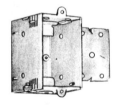

(ii)   **Sectional Boxes** − may be nailed on as shown.

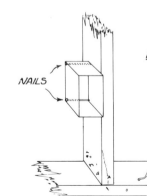

NOTE - THE BOX SHOWN HAS THE NAIL HOLES SET IN THE EXTREME CORNERS SO THAT THE NAILS WILL NOT INTERFERE WITH WIRE SPACE IN THE BOX. THIS BOX <u>MAY</u> BE NAILED ON.

3½ IN. NAILS MAY BE USED TO FASTEN THESE BOXES.

Note - If the supporting nails run **through** the box and if they are out of the way in the corners of the box as shown at left you need not reduce box fill. If the nails are forward as shown at right the permissible box fill given on page 74 must be reduced by one wire.

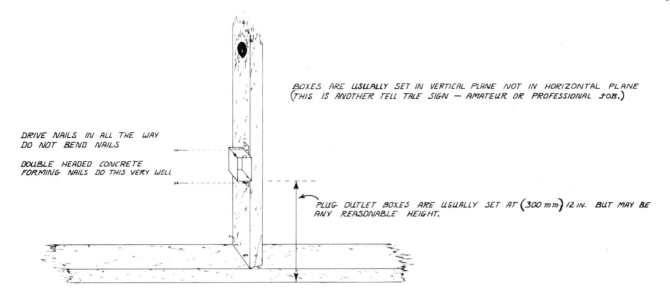

DRIVE NAILS IN ALL THE WAY
DO NOT BEND NAILS

DOUBLE HEADED CONCRETE
FORMING NAILS DO THIS VERY WELL

BOXES ARE USUALLY SET IN VERTICAL PLANE NOT IN HORIZONTAL PLANE
(THIS IS ANOTHER TELL TALE SIGN — AMATEUR OR PROFESSIONAL JOB.)

PLUG OUTLET BOXES ARE USUALLY SET AT (300 mm) 12 IN. BUT MAY BE
ANY REASONABLE HEIGHT.

(iii)   **Metal Gang Boxes** — Rule 12-3014

Check with your Inspector before fastening metal gang boxes with long nails, as shown.

THESE NAILS MUST BE LONG
ENOUGH TO ALLOW FOR APPROX 1¼ IN.
PENETRATION INTO THE STUD.

These metal boxes may be supported with a brace, as shown, or with wood backing.

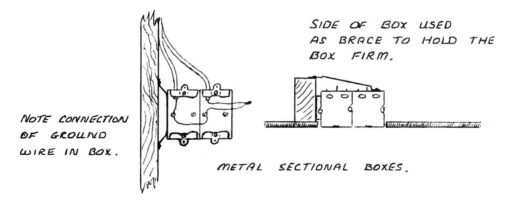

SIDE OF BOX USED
AS BRACE TO HOLD THE
BOX FIRM.

NOTE CONNECTION
OF GROUND
WIRE IN BOX.

METAL SECTIONAL BOXES.

Note — A simple method of supporting a metal gang box is to use one of the metal side plates which were removed to form the gang box. Use the side which has the nail—on lugs and fasten one end to the back of the gang box with one of the bonding screws installed from the back of the box. The other end of the brace is nailed to the stud, as shown.

An alternative method is to fasten the gang box to a wood member installed behind the box. This is usually an unhappy experience because of the many screws protruding through the back of the box.

(c) <u>**Set Flush**</u>

(i) Rule 12—3020 — Set all boxes so that they are flush with the finished surface. Pay particular attention to the feature walls of wood panelling. Don't forget to allow for the thickness of the wood strapping.

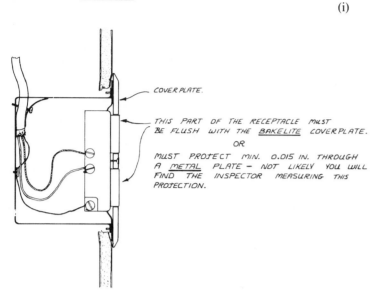

COVER PLATE.

THIS PART OF THE RECEPTACLE MUST
BE FLUSH WITH THE <u>BAKELITE</u> COVER PLATE.
OR
MUST PROJECT MIN. 0.015 IN. THROUGH
A <u>METAL</u> PLATE — NOT LIKELY YOU WILL
FIND THE INSPECTOR MEASURING THIS
PROJECTION.

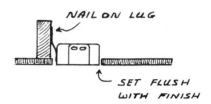

NAIL ON LUG

SET FLUSH
WITH FINISH

(ii)   **Box Extenders** — Approved box extenders must be used where the box is not flush with the finish.

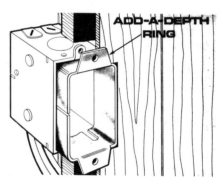

ADD-A-DEPTH RING

Where the box has been set for the wrong thickness of wall or ceiling finish and it is not flush as required, a simple box extension can be made with a section of plastic outlet box, as shown.

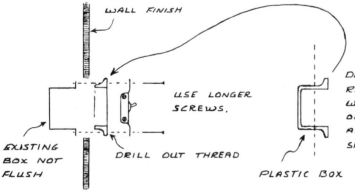

WALL FINISH

USE LONGER
SCREWS.

EXISTING
BOX NOT
FLUSH

DRILL OUT THREAD

PLASTIC BOX

DETERMINE DEPTH
REQUIRED, CUT
WITH HACK SAW
ON DOTTED LINE
AND INSTALL AS
SHOWN.

(d) **Bonding of Boxes** − Rules 12-626, 10-404, 10-808(2), 10-906 & Bulletin 10-1-0(11)(14)

The bare grounding conductor in the outlet box must be properly connected as shown below.

Note − the bare wire should:

(1) first connect to each box as shown.
  − in metal gang boxes it connects to each section.
  − in plastic gang boxes it connects to each metal strap inside the box unless these straps are already joined together by the manufacturer.

(2) next it connects to each bare wire entering the outlet box. See under "Conductor Joints & Splices" on page 78 for comments on method of joining these wires.

(3) last, it connects to the green grounding screw on the base of the plug receptacle.

THIS SHORT LENGTH OF WIRE FROM THE MARR CONNECTOR TO THE PLUG RECEPTACLE IS CALLED A PIGTAIL

As noted above, where there are two or more ground wires they must be properly joined and connected to both the box and receptacle. They may not be twisted together and wrapped around a bonding screw. Rule 10-808(2) and Bulletin 10-1-0(11) say that only one wire may be fastened to any one bonding screw. If you have two or more bonding wires connect one to the bonding screw in the box but leave it long enough so that the other wires can be spliced to it as shown.

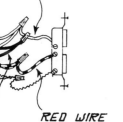

RED WIRE
BLACK WIRE

Pigtails Required- Rule 26-700(11) & Bulletin 26-2-0(2)

These rules require that the ground wires be joined as shown, so that any fixture may be removed temporarily without disconnecting the ground wire to other outlets on that circuit.

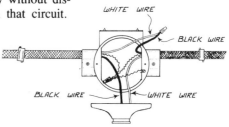

WHITE WIRE
BLACK WIRE
BLACK WIRE
WHITE WIRE

(e) **Wires in Box** − Rules 12-3002(4), 12-3040

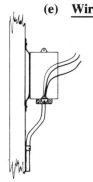

(i) **Free Conductor**

At least 150 mm(6 in.) of free conductor must be left in the outlet box to allow joints to be made or fixtures to be connected in a workmanlike manner.

(ii) **Cable Sheath** − Rule 2-108

The outer cable sheath should not project into the outlet box more than ½ in. past the connector. Remove this outer sheath as required before installing the cable in the connector. This sheath is very difficult to remove properly once the cable is actually installed.

(iii) **Box Fill**

Watch that box fill, it's tricky now. This otherwise simple problem has been made difficult in the code book. We must count the **number of wire connectors with insulated caps** which we install in a box. We must subtract the space occupied by these connector caps from the space in the box. Of course, we are stll required to note carefully the number of wires entering the box − deducting 1½ cu. inches for each **insulated #14 conductor. The bare conductor does not count. Then, the revised rules now say the switch or receptacle in the box occupies space equal to **two** conductors. **The tables below take all these factors into account.**

The following should be carefully noted:

  − Pigtails do **not** count as boxfill.
  − Boxes may have internal or external cable clamps − it does not matter. The boxfill is the **same** for both.
  − The wires from directly connected swag lamps do **not** count as box fill.

ACTUAL BOX FILL PERMITTED - RULE 12-3040

Box size and gang (See notes 2 to 6)	Cubic inch capacity		Maximum combination wires and caps using #14 wire								Maximum combination wires and caps using #12 wire							
Sectional metal box 3 x 2 x 1½ **Single gang**	8	Wires	3	3	2						2	2						
		Caps	0	1	2						0	1						
2 Gang Box	16	Wires	6	6	5	5	4				4	4	3					
		Caps	0	1	2	3	4				0	1	2					
3 Gang Box	24	Wires	9	9	8	8	7				6	6	5	5				
		Caps	0	1	2	3	4				0	1	2	3				
Sectional metal box. 3 x 2 x 2 / 3 x 2 x 2¼ **Single gang**	10	Wires	4	4	3	3					3	3	2					
		Caps	0	1	2	3					0	1	2					
2 Gang Box	20	Wires	8	8	7	7	6	6			6	6	5	5				
		Caps	0	1	2	3	4	5			0	1	2	3				
3 Gang Box	30	Wires	12	12	11	11	10	10			9	9	8	8	7			
		Caps	0	1	2	3	4	5			0	1	2	3	4			
Sectional Metal Box 3 x 2 x 2½ **Single gang**	12.5	Wires	6	6	5	5	4				5	5	4	4	3			
		Caps	0	1	2	3	4				0	1	2	3	4			
2 Gang Box	25	Wires	12	12	11	11	10	10	9	9	10	10	9	9	8	8		
		Caps	0	1	2	3	4	5	6	7	0	1	2	3	4	5		
3 Gang Box	37.5	Wires	18	18	17	17	16	16	15	15	15	15	14	14	13	13	12	12
		Caps	0	1	2	3	4	5	6	7	0	1	2	3	4	5	6	7
Plastic type box 3 x 2 x 2¾ **Single gang**	16	Wires	8	8	7	7	6	6			7	7	6	6	5	5		
		Caps	0	1	2	3	4	5			0	1	2	3	4	5		
Sectional Metal Box 3 x 2 x 3 **Single gang**	15	Wires	8	8	7	7	6	6			6	6	5	5	4			
		Caps	0	1	2	3	4	5			0	1	2	3	4			
2 Gang Box	30	Wires	16	16	15	15	14	14	13	13	12	12	11	11	10	10	9	
		Caps	0	1	2	3	4	5	6	7	0	1	2	3	4	5	6	
3 Gang Box	45	Wires	24	24	23	23	22	22	21	21	18	18	17	17	16	16	15	15
		Caps	0	1	2	3	4	5	6	7	0	1	2	3	4	5	6	7

NOTES ON BOX FILL TABLE

(1) Nominal Dimensions

Don't let the nominal box dimensions fool you. These are not the actual box sizes. It should be noted that some plastic (phenolic) box manufacturers keep the dimensions of their boxes close to the nominal. That is why the table on page 75 shows 16 cu. inches for a 2¾ in. deep **plastic** box but only 15 cu. in. for a 3 in. deep metal box. It is better to work from box volume than from it's dimensions.

(2) Various Combinations Given in the Table

In some combinations the tables allow many more connector caps than could possibly be used for the number of wires in the box. It also shows other combinations where there are not enough connector caps for the number of wires in the box. Choose a combination which will permit you to install at least the number of **wires** you need and at least the number of **connector caps** you require. For example, if we are using #14 loomex cable and intend to run a 3−wire cable and a 2−wire cable into a 2 in. deep switch box and plan to make 2 joints in this box the table says NO! It's too full. We may install only 4 − #14 wires and one connector cap in this box.

Note − only the insulated wires count as box fill − the bare wire does not count. A deeper box is required. The table shows a 2½ in. deep box may contain the 5 − #14 wires and the two splices (connector caps) we need. We do not need to provide the extra space as far as the rules are concerned but this is the combination nearest to our needs and it gives us room for a little error in our planning.

(3) Insulated Caps

The rule says if we use these, we must reduce the number of wires in the box. The table on page 75 takes all this into account. **Note** − this applies to insulated caps of all kinds.

(4) Tape Insulated Joints & Splices

The rule does not mention tape insulated joints or splices − perhaps it is because they occupy less space in the box. If you are using tape to insulate splices, you may add one conductor to the box fill indicated in the table. See also under "Conductor Joints & Splices" on page 75.

If for some reason you have misjudged and find you have more "things" in a box than the rules permit you to have, simply change from insulated caps to taped splices. These do not count as box fill.

(5) Bare Bonding Wires

These **wires** are in the box but are **not** counted as box fill − rule 12-3040(1).

Note − Insulated caps on connectors used to splice the bare bond wires **do count** as box fill − rule 12-3040(2) refers to "every" insulator cap. Insulation is really not required on bond wire splices − a crimp−on connector may be used without insulation.

Box size	Cubic inch capacity	OCTAGONAL BOXES	
		Maximum combination wires and caps using #14 wire	Maximum combination wires and caps using #12 wire
Metal octagonal box 4 x 1½in. deep.	15	**Wires** 10 10 9 9 8 8 **Caps** 0 1 2 3 4 5	8 8 7 7 6 6 0 1 2 3 4
Metal octagonal box 4 x 2 1/8 in. deep.	21	**Wires** 14 14 13 13 12 12 11 11 **Caps** 0 1 2 3 4 5 6 7	12 12 11 11 10 10 9 0 1 2 3 4 5 6

Box size	Cubic inch capacity	ROUND METAL BOXES	
Shallow saucer type box. Limited use rule 12-3002(4)	5	**Wires** 3 3 2 **Caps** 0 1 2	2 2 0 1

Box size	Cubic inch capacity	ROUND PLASTIC BOXES	
Round plastic box 4 x 1½ in deep.	14	**Wires** 9 9 8 8 7 7 **Caps** 0 1 2 3 4 5	8 8 7 7 6 0 1 2 3 4
Round plastic box 4 x 2 1/8 in. deep.	22	**Wires** 14 14 13 13 12 12 11 **Caps** 0 1 2 3 4 5 6	12 12 11 11 10 10 9 0 1 2 3 4 5 6
Round plastic box 4 x 2 5/8 in. deep	28	**Wires** 18 18 17 17 16 16 15 15 **Caps** 0 1 2 3 4 5 6 7	16 16 15 15 14 14 13 13 0 1 2 3 4 5 6 7

(f) <u>**Conductor Joints & Splices**</u> – Rules 4-034(4), 10–808(2)

    (i)   Pigtails Required – Rule 26-700(11) – Where a circuit supplies more than one plug outlet the joints and splices must be made as shown below. These are called pigtails.

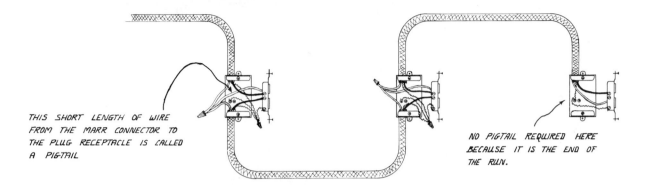

THIS SHORT LENGTH OF WIRE FROM THE MARR CONNECTOR TO THE PLUG RECEPTACLE IS CALLED A PIGTAIL

NO PIGTAIL REQUIRED HERE BECAUSE IT IS THE END OF THE RUN.

    Remember – Pigtails are required on bare bond wires. Rule 10-808(2)
    Pigtails are required on the neutral wires. Rule 4-034(4)
    Pigtails are required on the hot wires. Rule 26-700(11)

Such pigtails are required **in every case** where the circuit continues on to supply other outlets. Such splices **may not** be made with the terminal screws on the receptacle even though they may appear to be designed for that purpose.

    (ii)   <u>**In Boxes**</u> – Rule 12-606

Joints may be made only in outlet boxes or junction boxes. Junction boxes should be used **very sparingly** because you can get into more trouble with the Inspector when he finds them. Junction boxes may **not** be buried in the walls or ceilings.

    (iii)   <u>**Solder or Mechanical Joints & Splices**</u> – Rules 10-808(2), 10-906(2), 12-112

    Solder – This is probably the best possible method of splicing circuit conductors. It takes longer to make solder joints. Use a non–corrosive paste, usually 50/50 solder (50% tin 50% lead) for easy flowing and a minimum amount of heat. Then apply scotch electrical tape. Build up a layer of tape equal to the insulation thickness of the conductor. This is needed, not for dialectric strength, but for mechanical protection.

    Be sure to melt solder on wire.

SOLDER   SOLDERING PASTE

    Caution – Do not solder **bonding** conductors – crimp-on type may be used. Taping is not required.

    Don't try to cheat if you want to live to a ripe old age. If you are using the soldering method, use it, don't think you can get away with just twisting the wires together, then taping them without soldering the joint – your Inspector will find out and then – – – – – – –.

    Crimp-on – These are good if properly installed. Don't just gimble the connector with your pliers or side cutters and hope the Inspector will not see it. That is poor workmanship and is rejectable according to rule 2-108. Use an approved crimping tool or use the twist—on type wire connectors.

NEW WT1000 STA-KON® HAND TOOL will increase installing convenience of terminals, splices and wire joints on wire range from #22 to #10, insulated and uninsulated.

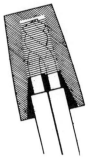

Twist-on Insulator Caps

There are a number of different types and sizes of twist—on wire connectors available. You must use the correct size to make a good electrical connection. Check the marking on the carton to determine the number of wires permitted in each connector.

(g) Junction Boxes

Accessibility - Rules 12-3018(1), 12-112 — They must remain accessible. This means they may not be hidden inside a wall or ceiling or similar place.

Head Clearance — Rule 12-3018(2) — Where junction boxes are installed in an attic or crawl space, there shall be at least 900 mm (35.4 in.) vertical space to provide access.

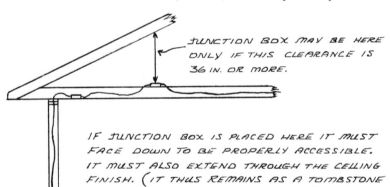

JUNCTION BOX MAY BE HERE ONLY IF THIS CLEARANCE IS 36 IN. OR MORE.

IF JUNCTION BOX IS PLACED HERE IT MUST FACE DOWN TO BE PROPERLY ACCESSIBLE. IT MUST ALSO EXTEND THROUGH THE CEILING FINISH. (IT THUS REMAINS AS A TOMBSTONE TO THE ERROR IN YOUR WIRING JOB)

Where To Use — Use junction boxes sparingly, only where you absolutely have to. Usually all your joints are made up in light, switch or plug outlet boxes.

14. LIGHTING FIXTURES

(a) Boxes Flush?

Check first if the boxes worked out flush with the wall or ceiling finish. If not, see page 73 for box extenders.

(b) Connections

Rules 30-314, 30-604 — When connecting light fixtures be sure to connect the neutral white or grey wire to the screw shell of the lamp holder and the black or hot wire to the center pin. The threaded portion of the lamp base must not be energized because of the danger of shock to a person replacing a lamp.

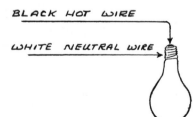

BLACK HOT WIRE

WHITE NEUTRAL WIRE

BECAUSE THE WHITE WIRE IS GROUNDED IT IS SAFE TO TOUCH THE SCREW SHELL WHEN REMOVING A LAMP.

(c) <u>**Bathroom**</u> — Rules 10-400, 30-326, 30-500, Bulletins 26-2-0(5), & 62-1-0(1)

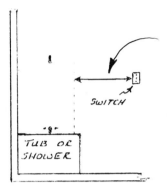

Light Fixtures — may be pendant type, such as swag lamps, provided that all the metal on the fixture is properly grounded.

NOTE — The metal on chain-hung fixtures **may not** be used to ground the fixture — a separate grounding conductor is required.

All switches must be kept out of reach of a person in a tub or shower. This means they must be at least 39.4 in. (1 m) away from a tub or shower.

Heat Lamps — Rules 30-200, 62-114, Bulletin 62-1-0(1) — Like any other recessed light fixture, bathroom heat lamps can be a very real fire hazard if improperly installed. Care should be taken to:

— locate the fixture away from the door so that it cannot radiate heat directly onto the upper edge of the door when it is left in the open position, see page 48. The bulletin also says the fixture must be at least 11.8 in (300 mm) from shower rods. The reason for this is that any clothes or towels left hanging on the door or on a shower rod would be too close to the fixture and could become overheated and cause a fire.

— enclose the fixture in a heat dissipator box as described on page 45.

(d) <u>**Fluorescent**</u> — Rule 30-312, Bulletin 12-11-0

Where this type of fixture is mounted end to end in a continuous row as in valance lighting the loomex cable (NMD-90) may enter only the first fixture. It must enter the fixture so that it need not run past the ballast. The connection from there to the other fixtures must be made with type A−18, GTF, R90 or similar types of wire. Care should be taken to see that all the fixtures in the row are properly grounded both for safety and for satisfactory operation.

(e) <u>**Basement**</u> — Rule 30-326(2)

Pull chain type fixtures must have an insulated link in the chain or have an approved insulating cord when used in the basement or similar area.

(f) <u>**Low Ceiling**</u> — Rule 30-318

Where fixtures are installed in a crawl space or attic, where there isless than 2.1 m(82.7 in.) headroom, the fixture shall be flexible type or be guarded.

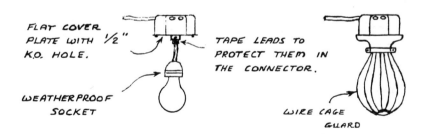

(g) <u>**Closet**</u> — Rule 30-204(2)

Fixtures may **not** be of pendant type. They should be located away from any possible contact with stored items in the closet. See diagram page 48.

15.   PLUG RECEPTACLES

(a) Boxes Flush?

Check first if the boxes worked out flush with the wall or ceiling finish. Check especially the outlets in feature walls. If they are not flush, see page 73 for box extenders.

(b) Polarization

This is an important detail. You will notice the receptacle has a brass terminal screw and a chrome plated terminal screw. Be sure to connect the black or sometimes the red wire to the brass terminal screw and the white neutral conductor connects to the chrome plated terminal screw. The Inspector has a little tester he uses to check this connection without removing any cover, etc. If you have connected incorrectly he will find it.

(c) **Type** — Rule 26-700 and Diagram 1, page 426 in the code

Polarized type receptacles must be used for all plug outlets except clock outlets.

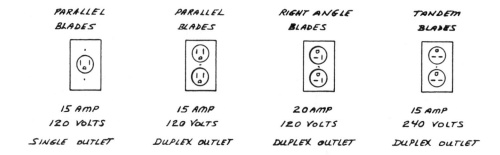

20 amp. 120 volt plug receptacles are **not interchangeable** with 15 amp. as the illustration shows. These should be wired with #12 (20 amp) wire and may be protected with a 20 amp. breaker or fuse.

15 amp. 240 volt plug receptacles are **non-interchangeable** with the 120 volt receptacles. Breakers supplying these outlets must have **tie-bars** or handles. Fuses must have switch or common pull arrangement as used for water heater or dryer. Rule 14-010, 14-302.

Split Receptacle — note the connection on this receptacle as shown on page 61.

(d) **Grounding** — Rules 10-808(2), 10-906 & Bulletin 10-1-0(11)(14)

The bare wire in each outlet box connects first to the box, then to the plug receptacle **in every case** as shown.

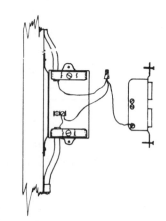

NOTE CONDUCTORS MUST LIE BETWEEN RAISED SECTIONS ON EACH SIDE OF SCREW.

(e) <u>**Bathroom Plug Receptacle**</u> — Rule 26-702(8)(9)(10)

Bathroom plug outlets must be either:

(i) a G.F.I. type recetacle; or

(ii) a standard type duplex plug receptacle **provided** it is supplied with special type circuit breaker at the panel. This breaker is called a Class A Ground Fault Interrupter. See also page 60.

(f) <u>**Outdoor Plug Receptacles**</u> — Rules 26-704(7), 12-3024, 26-706

Receptacles exposed to the weather shall be equipped with spring loaded or threaded cover plates to prevent moisture from entering.

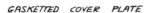

GASKETTED COVER PLATE

COVER HELD IN PLACE WITH ONE SCREW.

GASKET

NOTE - BOX IS SET IN ONE BOARD FACE WHICH PERMITS GASKET TO SEAL PROPERLY.

RECEPTACLES LOCATED UNDER A ROOF OVERHANG ARE PROTECTED FROM THE WEATHER.

THIS LOCATION IS ACCEPTABLE WITH STANDARD BOX AND COVERPLATE.

(g) <u>**Garden Outlets**</u>

Where outdoor outlet boxes are **free standing** as in a garden area for decorative lighting the outlet must:

- be in a weatherproof box — use an F.S. box or equal.
- be equipped with cover plates held in place with 4 screws.

- be very well grounded.
- be above grade.
- Bulletin 26-2-0(8) says these plug outlets must be G.F.I. protected with a special breaker at the panel or you may use a G.F.I. type receptacle. Treat these outlets as described under "Outdoor Outlets" on page 66.

The supply cable may be NMWU — #14 — depending on the length of run. Mechanical protection must be provided where it runs out of the trench and into the F.S. box.

Rigid metal conduit may be used to protect the cable and to support the box by using a horizontal bend in the trench to hold the conduit upright.

16. <u>HEAVY APPLIANCES</u> – RANGES, DRYERS, GARURATORS ETC.

(a) <u>General Information</u>

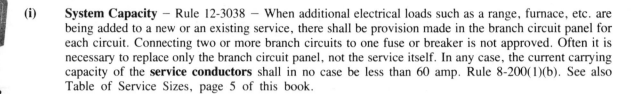

(i) **System Capacity** – Rule 12-3038 – When additional electrical loads such as a range, furnace, etc. are being added to a new or an existing service, there shall be provision made in the branch circuit panel for each circuit. Connecting two or more branch circuits to one fuse or breaker is not approved. Often it is necessary to replace only the branch circuit panel, not the service itself. In any case, the current carrying capacity of the **service conductors** shall in no case be less than 60 amp. Rule 8-200(1)(b). See also Table of Service Sizes, page 5 of this book.

(ii) **Control** – Rule 14-010(b) – requires that all 240 volt appliances must be provided with a device which will simultaneously disconnect both of the hot conductors at the point of supply.

Circuit Breakers require a tie-bar to fulfill this requirement. Rule 14-302(b)(i).

(iii) **Length of Run** – Any length up to 30 m (98 ft.) is acceptable. Longer runs may be acceptable too but they suggest there is a problem with the service location.

(iv) **Mechanical Protection** – Rule 12-618 – requires mechanical protection for loomex cable where it is run on the surface of a wall etc. and within 1.5 m (59 in.) from the floor. To comply with this rule, most Inspectors require a flexible conduit installed over the loomex cable supplying a furnace, garburator, etc.

(v) **Cable Strapping** – Rule 12-610 – Cable shall be properly strapped within 300 mm (11.8 in.) of cable termination and every 1.5 m(59 in.).

(vi) **Staples and Straps** – used to support cables shall be approved for the particular cable involved.

Note – Where cables run through holes in studs or joists they are considered properly strapped.

(vii) **Grounding** – Rules 10-400, 10-404 – All equipment must be adequately grounded. The bare wire in the supply cable must connect to the bonding screw in the branch circuit panel and to each appliance, using the bonding screw or the bolt provided. It is not enough to wrap the wire around a cable connector or cover screw. Too much depends on a good connection

(b) <u>Garburator</u> – Rules 28-106(1), 28-200, 28-600

You will require a separate two wire cable to supply the garburator. The supply cable may be #14 copper.

The supply cable should run into the control switch outlet box above the counter then down to the motor. You will require flexible conduit to protect the cable from a point inside the wall to the connector on the garburator.

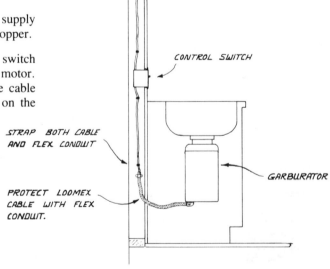

CONTROL SWITCH

STRAP BOTH CABLE AND FLEX CONDUIT

GARBURATOR

PROTECT LOOMEX CABLE WITH FLEX CONDUIT.

(c) <u>Dishwasher</u> - Rules 28-106(1), 28-200

This is a motor and heating load. These usually operate at 120 volts, therefore, a 2–wire cable is required. Unless you are absolutely sure your dishwasher can be served with a #14 cable you should install a #12 copper and 20 amp breaker. You will require a separate circuit. This cable may be run directly into the cable connector or the connection box on the dishwasher. Make sure that the bare wire is connected to the bonding terminal.

(d) <u>**Domestic Ranges**</u> − Rule 8-300

(i) <u>**Freestanding Type**</u> − Rules 26-746, 26-748 & Bulletin 26-3-0

Freestanding electric ranges must be cord connected. The plug receptacle required for this connection is a 3 pole, 4 wire grounding type as shown.

Note − This applies in every case. If for any reason the range is being replaced with a new or another used one, it must be cord connected. Bulletin 26-3-0 requires this even if the old range was direct connected.

Cable size .... #8 NMD7 copper
Outlet box size .... 4−11/16 x 4−11/16 x 2 ⅛
Plug receptacle rating .... 50 amp.
Rating of fuses or breakers .... 40 amp. each

FREE STANDING RANGE

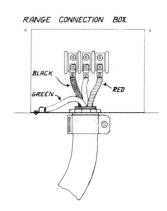

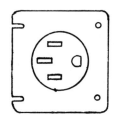

<u>Notes</u> − There are 3 rules to watch for:

(1) The range outlet box must be located very near the mid−point on the wall behind the range,

AND,

(2) This range outlet box must not be higher than 100 mm (4 in.) above the floor to the center of the outlet box,

AND,

(3) This outlet box must be carefully positioned so that when the receptacle is finally installed, the ground pin will be either on the right hand or the left hand but not at the top or the bottom.

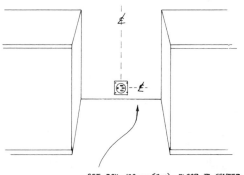

This means we must know exactly where the range will be located. Then find the center line and mark that on the wall. Next, measure 4 inches up from the floor along that center line and mark it. That is the precise location of the range outlet box. It's like taking aim with a canon to shoot a flea.

(ii)   **Drop—in Type**

This is the conventional range but it is not free standing. It is fitted into the kitchen cabinets.

Cable size ....#8 NMD7 copper
Outlet box size ....box not needed
Flexible conduit size ....¾ inch
Rating of fuses or breakers ....40 amp.

This unit is not cord connected. The #8 NMD7 cable may be run directly into the connection box.

DROP-IN RANGE

Note – The supply cable must be protected with ¾ inch flexible conduit for the last 3 feet or so at the range and where it may be subject to mechanical damage.

(iii)   **Built—in Type** – Rule 26-744

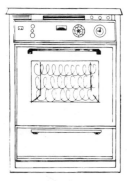

main cable size ....#8 NMD7 copper
Flexible conduit size ....¾ inch

Cable to **oven** size ....#10 NMD7
Flexible Conduit size ....½ inch
Rating of fuses or breakers ....40 amp. each

Note – The above sizes are sufficient for the average 12 kw. range

Branch Circuit Protection – Most range units are equipped with overcurrent protection (fuses or mini-breakers) for the individual elements. If it is not provided as part of each unit, it must be installed by the customer. Rule 26-744. This usually consists of a 6 circuit fuse panel. The branch circuit wires to the elements are normally provided by the manufacturer but they must be connected to the fuse panel by the installer. Each unit also has a length of supply cable attached.

BUILT-IN OVEN

Wiring to Units – Rule 26-744(2)&(3) – The electrical load in the cooking tops is usually greater than in the oven. Therefore, the junction box is located near the cooking tops so that the supply cable provided by the manufacturer is long enough to run directly into it as shown. The #10 cable to the oven can also be run into this junction box.

SEPARATE SURFACE UNITS

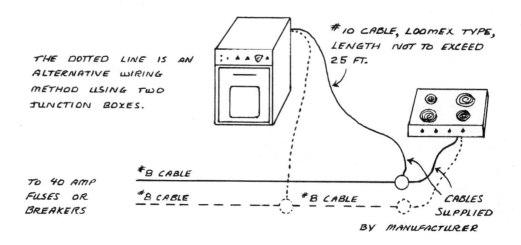

THE DOTTED LINE IS AN ALTERNATIVE WIRING METHOD USING TWO JUNCTION BOXES.

#10 CABLE, LOOMEX TYPE, LENGTH NOT TO EXCEED 25 FT.

TO 40 AMP FUSES OR BREAKERS

#8 CABLE

#8 CABLE

#8 CABLE

CABLES SUPPLIED BY MANUFACTURER

Note — Rule 26-744(2)&(3) — The tap cable to the oven must not be longer than 7.5 m (24.6 ft.). Where the units are too far apart for a 24.6 ft. cable, a second junction box may be installed (shown by dotted line) but the #8 supply cable must continue on to the junction box at the cooking tops unless this load is 7200 watts or less.

Cable Protection — Flexible conduit is required on these cables for mechanical protection, even though they are in a cabinet below the range. See also rule 12-618.

Grounding — If you do not connect the bare ground conductor properly at the panel and at the range, one day the chief cook may not be alive to greet you with a kiss at the end of a busy day.

(e) Dryers — Rules 26-746(3)&(4) & Bulletin 26-3-0

Electrical dryers must be cord connected to comply with the new code rules. Use a 3 pole, 4 wire grounding type plug receptacle as shown at left.

Note — This applies in every case. If for any reason the dryer is being replaced with a new or another used one, it must be cord connected. Bulletin 26-3-0 requires this even if the old dryer was direct connected.

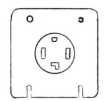

30 AMP DRYER RECEPTACLE

Cable size ....#10 NMD7 copper
Outlet box size ....4 11/16 x 4 11/16 x 2 ⅛ in.
Plug receptacle rating ....30 amp.
Rating of fuses or breakers ....30 amp. each

These sizes are sufficient for most dryers, i.e. dryers with ratings not greater than 7200 watts.

The bare grounding conductor must be properly connected at the panel and at the dryer to ensure safety to the operator.

(f) Water Heater — Bulletin 8-1-0(6)

Cable size .... #12 NMD7 copper
Flexible conduit size .... 7/16 inch
Rating of fuses or breakers .... 20 amp.
Note — Fuse must be Type D ...... Rule 14-610

Note — These sizes refer to water heaters with ratings from 3 kw. (3000 watts) up to 3.8 kw. (3800 watts).

(i) Circuit — Rule 26-752(4) — must be on a separate circuit with sufficient capacity to carry the maximum possible load that may be connected at one time by the thermostat. Most tanks are provided with 2 — 3 kw. elements, only one of which can operate at one time. According to rule 8-302(3) and bulletin 8-1-0(6), water heater loads are considered continuous and must therefore not be loaded to more than 80% of the rating of the breaker or fuse. A 3 kw. water heater draws 12.5 amps at 240 volts but the largest continuous load permitted on a 15 amp circuit is 80% or 12 amp. We therefore require 12.5 x 10 ÷ 8 = 15.6 amp or 20 amp breaker or fuse and #12 cable.

NOTE CABLE STRAPPING
IF THIS IS NOT POSSIBLE
TAPE FLEX TO LOOMEX
CABLE AT THIS POINT.

USE 7/16 IN. FLEXIBLE CONDUIT
OVER SUPPLY CABLE.

POSITION TANK SO THAT THE
NAMEPLATE IS ACCESSIBLE.
RULE 2-118

Rule 4-034(1) permits a 2-conductor loomex cable to be used to supply a 240 volt load. When this is done the white wire is not used as a neutral but is hot. Wherever this white wire is visible, as in a junction box etc. it must be painted or taped to show a colour other than white, grey or green.

(ii) **Cable Protection** − Rules 12-618, 12-1104 − Protect loomex cable with 7/16 inch flexible conduit where exposed to mechanical injury.

(g) <u>**Furnace (gas or oil)**</u> − Rule 26-806(2)

Gas Furnace

    Cable size ....#14 copper
    Flexible conduit size ....7/16 inch
    Fuse or breaker size ....15 amp.

Oil Furnace

    Cable size ....#12 copper
    Flexible Conduit size ....7/16 inch
    Fuse or breaker size ....20 amp.

(i) **Disconnect Switch** − Rules 26-806, 28-600

A disconnect switch is required for each furnace.

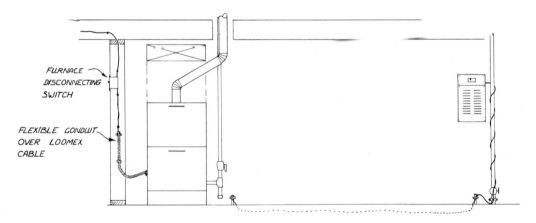

Location − A circuit breaker in a branch circuit panel may serve as disconnect switch provided it is located between the furnace and the escape route.

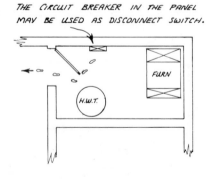

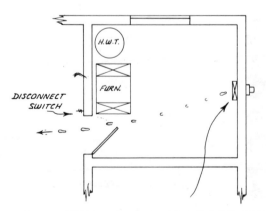

(ii) **Protection** — Rule 26-802 — The loomex cable is run in a 7/16 inch flexible conduit for the last few feet near the furnace where it is less than 1.5 m (59 in.) from the floor or where subject to damage.

(iii) **Cable Fastening** — The supply cable to the furnace may be run along the gas piping to the furnace. It may be fastened to the piping every 12 inches or so with several layers of friction tape. Check with your Inspector.

(iv) **Grounding** — Rule 10-400 — Be sure to connect securely the bare grounding conductor on the supply cable to the grounding terminal in the furnace junction box.

(v) **Gas Piping** — Rule 10-406(4) — This revised rule says we will accept the grounding conductor in the supply cable as adequate grounding for the furnace or boiler and it's piping. Be sure to connect this bare grounding conductor to the bonding terminal in the furnace or boiler connection box — that's all there is to it.

(h) Kitchen Fan

```
Cable size  ,,,,,,,,,,,,,,,,,,,,,,,,,,,,,,,,,,,,,,#14 NMD7 copper
Flexible conduit size .........................7/16 inch
Fuse or breaker rating .......................15 amp.
```

(i) The kitchen fan need not be on a separate circuit. It may be on a light or plug circuit but it **may not** be on any appliance circuit, rule 26-704. It is counted as one outlet when determining circuit loading.

(ii) **Cable Protection** — Rule 12-618 — Protect loomex cable with 7/16 inch flexible conduit **where it is exposed**. This includes that portion of the cable where it is exposed inside the cabinet where it may be subject to damage. Flexible cable must terminate in a flex connector at the fan and be strapped or taped to the loomex cable **before** it emerges from the wall.

(iii) **Grounding** — Rule 10-400 — Because it is near grounded objects it is very important to connect the bare ground wire securely to the ground terminal in the fan connection box.

(i) Hydromassage Bathtub

(i) **CSA Certified Units** — Make sure the unit you install has a CSA certification label. This may seem like a picky point but in fact, it is extremely important. It becomes convincingly so when you feel that tingly feeling in the rear while soaking in the tub after a hard day.

(ii) **Separate Circuit Required** — Rule 28-106(1) - For the rough wiring stage run a separate 2—wire loomex cable to the motor location. Later when the unit is actually installed you will need to install a disconnect switch at the motor location.

(iii) **Disconnect Switch Required** — Rule 28-600, 28-604(f). These rules require a disconnect switch for this motor. This may be a standard wall switch, such as is used to control light outlets. Don't forget to note the ampere rating of this switch — it must be 125% as great as the ampere rating of the pump motor.

Note — This is not a hot tub. It is a hydro—massage unit only. A hot tub usually has an electric heating element as well as a pump.

One more thing — do not forget to provide access to this motor and disconnect switch for maintenance purposes.

(iv) **G.F.C.I. Required** — Rule 68-300. This motor circuit must be protected with a G.F.C.I. Because this is a motor load this special circuit breaker may not supply any other load.

(v) **Lights and Plugs** — Rule 68-304. The usual rules for lights and plugs in bathrooms apply to this special bathroom.

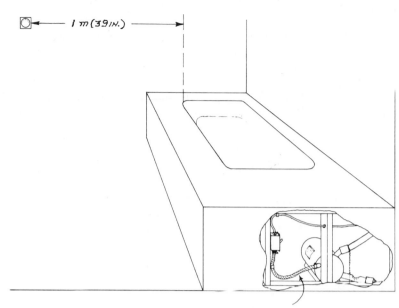

THIS CABLE MAY REQUIRE FLEXIBLE
CONDUIT IF SUBJECT TO MECHANICAL DAMAGE.

(vi)   **Control** – Rule 68-302

–   **Timer Required** – The controller must be a shut–off timer with a **maximum** time rating of 30 minutes.

–   **Location** – It must be at least 1 m. (39.4 in.) away from the tub. The rule does say this must be measured in a horizontal line.

17.   ELECTRIC HEATING – baseboards.

(a)   Rough Floor Map Required

The Electrical Inspector will want a rough sketch of the floor plan of your house showing:

–   the location of heaters
–   the rating of each heater
–   what circuit it is on
–   size of conductors and,
–   rating of breakers

Be sure your sketch is accurate and clear – easy to follow. Your Inspector will want it for that first rough inspection.

(b)   Building Insulation – Rule 62-112

Building insulation shall be of non–combustible type. It is not considered safe to install electric heating in walls or ceilings which have wood shavings or similar insulation. (Building Inspectors probably would'nt like it either).

(c)   Branch Circuits – Rule 62-108

Branch circuits which supply electric heaters may not be used to supply any other load.

2 Wire Cables – electric heaters are usually connected for 240 volts – no connection to the neutral. Rule 4-034(1) permits a 2–wire loomex cable with one black and one white wire to be used for these loads.

(d)   Breakers – Tie–bars – Rule 14-302(b)(i)

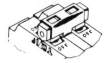 Breakers require tie–bars when used to supply 240 volt appliances such as heaters. The tie-bar is used to mechanically connect the operating handles of the breakers so that they operate as one.

(e) Circuit Loading

REDUCED LOADING — Rule 62-110(6) & (7)

In this new edition of the code this rule was **not** revised. This means we must **reduce** the load to 80% on branch circuits supplying electric baseboard heaters.

The following examples indicate circuit loadings permissible under the rules. The actual wattage rating and the number of heaters used need not be as shown provided the **sum** of the ratings of all the heaters on the circuit **does not exceed** the maximum permitted for that circuit.

Note — The sum of the connected loads may be 100% of the conductor ampacity but **must not exceed** 80% of the fuse or breaker rating. Rule 62-110(6).

All these tacky details are taken into account in the illustrations below.

15 Amp Circuit

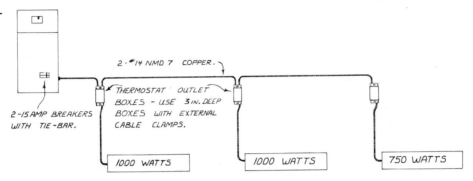

Maximum Length of this circuit run is 31.1 m. (102 ft.).

A 15 amp. 240 volt circuit using #14 loomex can supply 80% of 15 x 240 or 2880 watts. The total connected load on this circuit therefore **must not exceed 2880 watts.**

20 Amp. Circuit

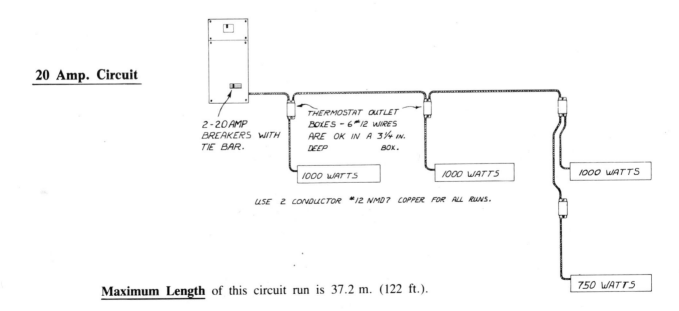

Maximum Length of this circuit run is 37.2 m. (122 ft.).

A 20 amp. 240 volt circuit using #12 loomex cable may supply 80% of 20 x 240 or 3840 watts. The total connected load on this circuit **must not exceed 3840 watts.**

30 Amp Circuit

This is the maximum size fuse or breaker permitted for electric heating in a residence except for central hot air furnace units. This 30 amp circuit is not used very often and it is not recommended.

A 30 amp. 240 volt circuit using #10 loomex may supply 80% of 30 x 240 or 5760 watts. The total connected load on this circuit **must not exceed 5760 watts.**

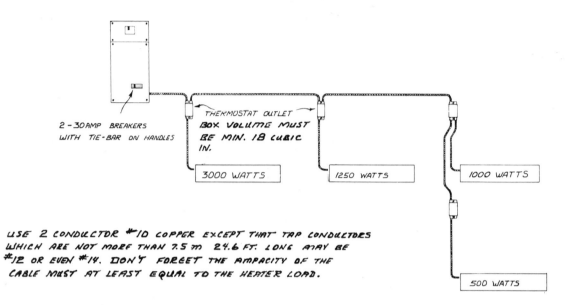

2 - 30 AMP BREAKERS
WITH TIE-BAR ON HANDLES

THERMOSTAT OUTLET
BOX VOLUME MUST
BE MIN. 18 CUBIC
IN.

3000 WATTS   1250 WATTS   1000 WATTS

500 WATTS

USE 2 CONDUCTOR #10 COPPER EXCEPT THAT TAP CONDUCTORS
WHICH ARE NOT MORE THAN 7.5 m 24.6 FT. LONG MAY BE
#12 OR EVEN #14. DON'T FORGET THE AMPACITY OF THE
CABLE MUST AT LEAST EQUAL TO THE HEATER LOAD.

Maximum Length of this circuit run to the farthest heater is 36.6 m. (120 ft.) plus thermostat run of 7.5 m(24.6 ft.)

(i)   The fuse or breaker rating must not exceed 30 amps.

   Note − This means that the minimum conductor ampacity must be 80% of 30 = 24 amps. A #10 copper conductor may be used.

(ii) The tap conductor must have a current carrying capacity of not less than ⅓ the rating of the branch circuit fuse or breaker ahead of it.

   Note − The #10 conductor need not be run all the way to the last heater and thermostat. It may be reduced to #14 copper provided this smaller conductor is not more than 7.5 m. (24.6 ft.) long.

(iii) The tap conductor may not be more than 7.5 m. (24.6 ft.) long as shown.

(f)   Bathroom Heat Lamp − Rule 62-108(3)

Heat lamps in bathrooms are normally supplied from lighting or plug outlet circuits. They may not be supplied from electric heating circuits.

Courtesy Canadian Chromalox Co. Ltd.

(g)   Thermostats

(i)   **Location** − Rule 62-202 requires a thermostat in each room where electric heating is installed.

   Location − According to Rule 62-202(2) & Bulletin 26-2-0(5) the thermostat must be kept at least 39.4 in. (1 m.) away from the inside wall of a tub or shower. This applies to **all** thermostats. Those separately mounted on the wall and those built into the heater itself.

   Note − if the heater is **not** equipped with a built−in thermostat it may be located within 39.4 in. of the tub or shower.

   Watch this one − in the **rough wiring stage** − make provisions for that thermostat.

    (ii)   **Rating** − Rule 62-128(1) − Those thermostats which are connected directly into the line and control the full load current must have a current rating at least equal to the **sum** of the current ratings of all the equipment they control.

    (iii)   **Type** − Rule 62-128(2) accepts thermostats whether they are marked with an indicating "off" position or not, sub−rule (2) of this rule merely indicates that if a thermostat has a marked "off" position that it must then open all ungrounded conductors of the controlled heating circuit. If the thermostat only indicates a high and a low position with graduated markings between, it need not open all ungrounded conductors of the circuit. Therefore, a single pole thermostat which does not have a marked "off" position would be acceptable on a normal 240 volt heating circuit.

(h) Outlet Boxes − Rules 12-606, 12-3002(5), Bulletins 12-11-0 & 62-1-0(2)

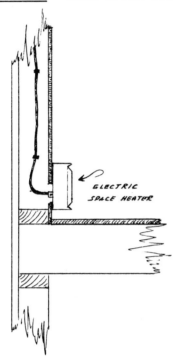

ELECTRIC SPACE HEATER

Location − An outlet box is not required. Bulletin 62-1-0 permits two cables to enter the connection box in electric baseboard heaters. Where more than two cables are required (in most cases you require three) the cables may be run into a junction box set flush into the wall behind the heater. This is perhaps the poorest method of connection to use because the boxes must be very accurately located to ensure they will be behind the heater and that they will be properly covered when the heater is installed. Bonding is a problem with this arrangement and finally, access to splices in the box is unsatisfactory. Avoid this method if possible. It is better to run these cables into the thermostat outlet boxes as shown in the 15 amp. and 20 amp. circuit illustrations above. Only one cable need enter the heater and this should run in directly without a connection box.

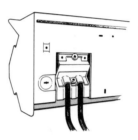

(i) Cable Protection − Rule 12−618

Where part of the cable is run exposed to mechanical injury, use a short length of EMT conduit or flexible conduit to protect the cable. Be sure to terminate the conduit in an approved manner so that it is grounded.

(j) Grounding − Rules 10-400, 10-906

The bare grounding wire (the code now calls this a bonding wire) in the supply cable must be securely connected to the fixture with the grounding terminal screw in each fixture.

18.   ELECTRIC HOT AIR FURNACE − Rule 62-222 & Bulletin 62-1-0(3)

Installing an electric hot air furnace is not as difficult as it may appear. By following these basic instructions carefully, you can do it and save.

(a) Clearances − Rule 62-222

This rule does not specify any minimum clearance but it does draw attention to two basic clearances required.

    (1) From Combustible Surfaces − observe all the clearances specified on the name plate and,

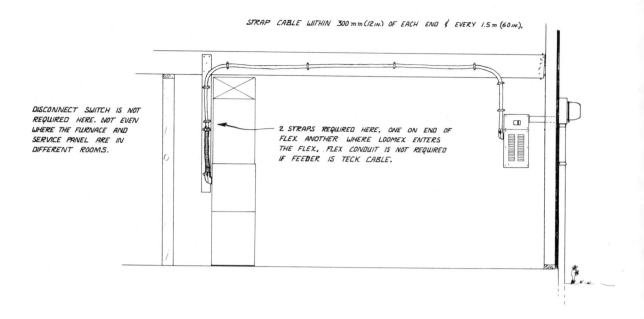

STRAP CABLE WITHIN 300mm (12IN.) OF EACH END & EVERY 1.5m (60IN.).

DISCONNECT SWITCH IS NOT REQUIRED HERE. NOT EVEN WHERE THE FURNACE AND SERVICE PANEL ARE IN DIFFERENT ROOMS.

2 STRAPS REQUIRED HERE. ONE ON END OF FLEX ANOTHER WHERE LOOMEX ENTERS THE FLEX. FLEX CONDUIT IS NOT REQUIRED IF FEEDER IS TECK CABLE.

(2) **For Maintenance** — do not install your furnace in a small confined space unless it is designed and marked for installation in an alcove or closet. There must be sufficient clearance to allow removal of panel covers and for maintenance work.

Note - Bulletin 62-1-0(3) is very specific. It says the requirements of rule 2-308 must be applied to this furnace. This means that there must be a clear working space, at least 39.4 in. **horizontal** space, in front of the furnace. This new bulletin also says that the **vertical** head room in that working space must be at least 39.4 in. (1 m.) high. These are minimum clearances. It may mean that some crawl spaces will not be acceptable locations for the electrical furnace because there is insufficient clearance.

(b) Supply to Furnace — Rule 62-110(6)&(7)

Below is a greatly simplified table of sizes. Use this table to determine the rating of the furnace supply cable and circuit breakers.

Note — The table takes into account the current drawn by the fan motor.

Your furnace size in kw.	Total Load Amps	Minimum Circuit Breaker Size Required	Size of Conductor to Furnace
5	22	30	#10 copper NMD7 (loomex) copper
10	43	70	#6 copper NMD7 (loomex) or teck - copper
15	64	100	#4 copper NMD7 (loomex) or teck - copper
18	77	100	#4 copper NMD7 (loomex) or teck - copper
20	85	125	#3 copper NMD7 (loomex) or teck - copper
24	103	150	#2 copper NMD7 (loomex) or teck - copper
27	116	150	#2 copper NMD7 (loomex) or teck - copper

The above table is based on CHROMALOX SPEC. sheet CCSL 266-4, dated Oct. 18/82.

(c) Furnace Disconnect switch — Rule 62-222(3)

Rule 62-222(3) has been amended for use in B.C. A disconnect switch is **not** required at the furnace.

(d) Wiring Method

NMD-90 cable. This is the new name for the old NMD7 loomex cable. This cable may be used if the size you need is available. All the usual rules for running loomex cable apply to this cable, i.e. strap it, protect it, and terminate it in approved cable connectors.

Teck Cable (copper) may also be used to supply the furnace. This is a tougher cable — it may not need any additional protection from mechanical injury.

Dry type cable connectors may be used indoors.

Note — peel off the PVC outer sheath, only at the connector, so that it (the connector) is clamped directly onto the metal armour.

(e) Mechanical Protection Required

Teck Cable has an aluminum armour and can take a little abuse, however, if there is any doubt, provide protection for the cable especially those sections which are run on the surface below the 5 ft. level.

NMD7 or NMD-90 — Loomex Cable — has no armour and therefore must always be protected from mechanical damage where it is run on the surface below the 5 ft. level. Rule 12-618. Use a flex conduit, sized large enough to allow the cable to move freely, for those sections where mechanical protection is needed.

Note — This flex conduit must then terminate in a flex connector at the furnace.

Consider using an angle connector at the furnace because this cable may not be bent sharply without damaging it.

(f) Thermostat Control Wiring

Table 19 in the code lists only one cable acceptable for low voltage thermostat control work. That is the type LVT cable. Truth is, Table 19 does list a type ELC cable for class 2 wiring but Rule 16-210(3) says it may not be used for heating control circuits. So we'r stuck with LVT cable only.

Strapping — Whatever staples or straps you use make sure they do not damage the sheath. Staples should be driven in only till they contact the cable. When a staple is driven in too deeply and short circuits the conductors, it turns the furnace on and there is nothing to shut it off, automatically, except the high limit safety device inside the furnace. The thermostat cable is important — install it carefully.

(g) Grounding — Rules 10-400, 10-600

Make certain the grounding conductor is properly connected, with approved lugs, at each end. Look for a separate grounding lug in the furnace connection box and in the service panel.

19. DRIVEWAY LIGHTING

(a) Conduit System

Rule 12-012 states that the conduit shall be buried to a depth of 450 mm. (17.7 in.) or if in an areas subject to vehicular traffic, e.g. under a driveway, to a depth of 600 mm. (23.6 in.).

Conduit is very seldom used for this work. It is difficult to properly terminate the conduit at either end. Don't forget, a bare grounding conductor must be drawn into the conduit along with the circuit conductors to ground the light standard.

Polyethylene pipe certified for at least 50 P.S.I. working pressure may be used for the **underground portion only**. It need not be CSA certified for electrical use. The riser at the house must be rigid P.V.C. or rigid metal conduit. Bulletin 12-2-0.

(b) Direct Burial − Rule 12-012

Depth of Burial − Type NMWU or NMW10 loomex cable, size #14, may be used as shown in the illustration. It shall be buried to a depth of 600 mm. (23.6 in.) or if it passes under a roadway or driveway, to a depth of 900 mm. (35.4 in.).

This depth may be reduced by 6 in. (150 mm.) if the cable is protected with treated planking as shown in the illustration, note the lesser depth shown.

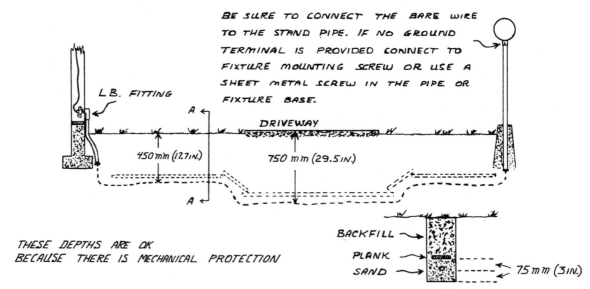

1 − **Sand or Earth** − may be used but note the stuff is to be screened with 6 mm. (¼ in.) screen. Cables should lie on 75 mm. (3 in.) thick bed of this screened sand or earth and have a further 75 mm. (3 in.) thick blanket of screened sand placed on top of the cables.

2 − **Treated Planking**− 2 in. untreated cedar planking is accepted in most cases. The rule says a 38 mm. (1½ in.) **treated** plank is required.

3 − **Section of Conduit** − This is to protect the cable from damage.

Rule 12-012(5) requires that this conduit terminate in a vertical position approximately 300 mm. (11.8 in.) above the trench floor. The cable must continue on downward, as shown, to allow movement during frost heaving.

Size of Conduit − is not critical. It should be large enough to be drawn in easily and without damage to the insulation.

Type of Conduit − may be rigid metal conduit or P.V.C. but **may not** be EMT, rule 12-1502, 22-500.

(c) Grounding − Rules 10-400, 10-906

It is very important that the ground wire be securely connected to the lamp standard.

20. TEMPORARY CONNECTION TO PERMANENT BUILDING

This is often referred to as TPB. It is really a permanent type of service connection but it is on a temporary basis until the wiring is entirely completed. Many of the building contractors now ask for this connection to speed up the finishing work. Check with your Inspector before attempting to prepare the installation for such a connection.

(a) Requirements for Connection

To obtain this connection, in most districts the following is required.

Service — Service must be entirely complete, including;

- meter backing
- meter blank cover
- weather seal below meter
- dux seal in last fitting, where required. See page 19 or 25.
- service grounding
- waste pipe bonding(note: both septic and soap systems must be bonded if they are metallic.
- panel covers must be installed.

Permits — must be complete, that is, they must cover the entire installation, including such appliances as range, water heater, dryer, furnace wiring etc. even though these appliances are not yet installed at the time the temporary connection is required.

One branch circuit must be completed by installing all fixtures, plates etc. but **leave all other circuits** disconnected unless these too are entirely completed. Do not energize any circuit which runs through an outdoor outlet box unless it is entirely complete with fixtures, fittings, plates, covers etc. It is better to choose a circuit which has all it's outlets facing **indoors**.

In addition, most localities require a temporary connection permit (or TCP) before the Inspector can authorize the power utility to connect the service.

Building — In some localities it is necessary to close the building for this connection. That is, it must have doors and windows installed before the service can be authorized for connection. Check with your local Inspector.

Identify House — The house number should be posted in a conspicuous place on the house. This is to help the Inspector and the power utility connection crew to identify the correct house quickly.

Completion — When the installation is entirely complete, notify the Inspection department immediately. The Provincial Government Inspector requires written notification (this may be a permit stub properly signed and dated or a special form may need to be filled in). Check with your Inspector. If the temporary permit expires before the installation is completed, you will need to renew this connection permit.

Special Cases. Check with your Inspector first.
For Underground Services Only

It is not always necessary to frame the whole building, i.e. put on the roof and outside sheathing to get a temporary to permanent connection, as described above. Often it is possible to have the building contractor erect only a small portion of the permanent wall where the permanent service (meter base and service panel) is to be located. The permanent meter base and service panel along with one or more plug outlets may then be installed on this partial wall. A temporary wooden enclosure similar to that described for temporary construction service on page 98, must be built to protect this equipment from the weather and small prying and inquisitive fingers from getting hurt.

Service Grounding — Permanent service grounding should be installed. This usually consists of 2 — 1.8 m(70.9 in.) rods 2 m(78.7 in.) apart. Don't forget to connect the water piping system when it is installed. See page 34 for more detailed instructions.

21 TEMPORARY POLE SERVICES - Section 76 in the Code & Bulletin 6-6-0(4)(5) & (6)

(a) Minimum Service Size

Wire size ....#10
Conduit size ....¾ inch
Circuit breaker or Fuse ratings ....15, 20 or 30 amp.

Circuit Breaker or Fuse Rating − Rule 28-200 − Circuit breakers or fuses may be 20 amp. or for the larger power saw loads, may be as high as 30 amp. even though the receptacle is rated for only 15 amp.

(b) Pole Requirements

(i)   **Solid** − It must be a solid timber. Laminated timber is **not** acceptable.

(ii) **Size** − Minimum size is 150 mm by 150 mm (6 in. by 6 in.) timber, or if a round pole is used, it must have a 150 mm. (6 in.) diameter top.

(iii) **Length** − Minimum length is 5 m (16.4 ft.). This provides for 1.2 m. (47.2 in.) in the ground and a minimum 4.3 m. (14.1 ft.) above ground. This is acceptable only where lines are short and the Hydro pole is on your side of the road.

  Lines crossing public roadway must be 5.5 m (18 ft.) high.
  Lines Crossing areas accessible to pedestrians only must be a minimum 3.5 m . (11.5 ft.) high.

(iv) **Gain** − Two shallow saw cuts approximately 2 inches apart, with wood chip between removed, marking the pole 3.7 m. (12.1 ft.) from butt end.

(v)   **Bracing** − as required to offset the pull of the Hydro lines. This should be done with 50 mm x 100 mm. (4 in. x 2 in.) lumber attached as high as possible and should make an angle approximately 30 degrees with the pole.

(c) Meter Base

(i)   **Height** − maximum 2100 mm (6.9 ft.) grade level to bottom of meter.

(ii) **Blank Cover** − Wood blank cover may be required on the meter base - check with your Inspector.

(iii) **Connection** − Connections are as shown on page 98.

(d) Service Equipment

TYPE S.

FUSE

INSERT

(i)   **Circuit Breaker Type** − This is the preferred type of equipment for temporary construction services.

  Note − Rule 14-302 requires a double pole breaker with **single** handle be used. Two breakers with a tie-bar on the handles **is not** acceptable for this purpose because this is a **service** switch.

(ii) **Fuse Type** − Rule 14-204 − Non−interchangeable type fuses only may be used. This means that fuse adapters must be installed in the standard fuse sockets in the switch and panel. These adapters are available in different sizes or current ratings. Once a particular adapter has been installed, say a 20 amp. size, only a 20 amp. fuse will fit this socket.

  Please note: In some districts only circuit breaker type equipment is permitted. You should check with your local Inspector before proceeding.

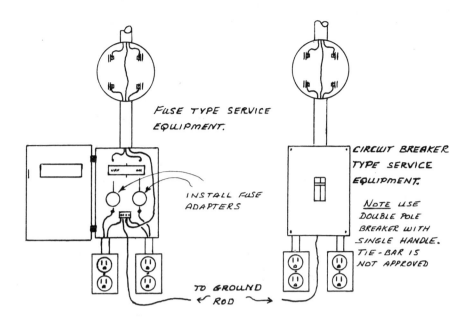

FUSE TYPE SERVICE EQUIPMENT.

INSTALL FUSE ADAPTERS

CIRCUIT BREAKER TYPE SERVICE EQUIPMENT.

NOTE USE DOUBLE POLE BREAKER WITH SINGLE HANDLE. TIE-BAR IS NOT APPROVED

TO GROUND ROD

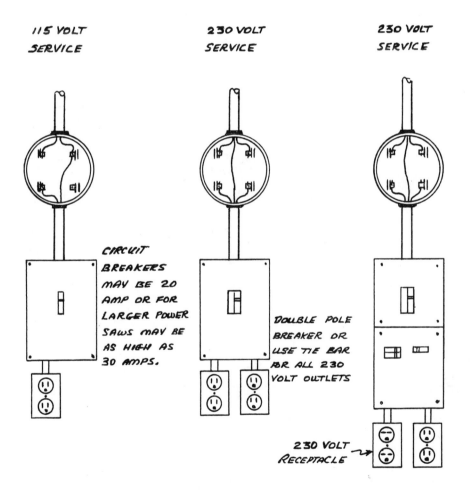

115 VOLT SERVICE

230 VOLT SERVICE

230 VOLT SERVICE

CIRCUIT BREAKERS MAY BE 20 AMP OR FOR LARGER POWER SAWS MAY BE AS HIGH AS 30 AMPS.

DOUBLE POLE BREAKER OR USE TIE BAR FOR ALL 230 VOLT OUTLETS

230 VOLT RECEPTACLE

(e) Service Enclosures

Standard Non-Weatherproof Type — Non-weatherproof service equipment may be used if it is installed in a solidly constructed **weatherproof** box. This box may be of lumber or plywood not less than 20 mm (¾ in.) in thickness with hinged door and lock. If practicable, the door should be hinged at the top.

STANDARD EQUIPMENT IN WOODEN ENCLOSURES

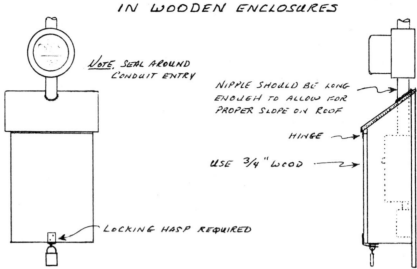

<u>Note.</u> SEAL AROUND CONDUIT ENTRY

NIPPLE SHOULD BE LONG ENOUGH TO ALLOW FOR PROPER SLOPE ON ROOF

HINGE →

USE 3/4" WOOD →

← LOCKING HASP REQUIRED

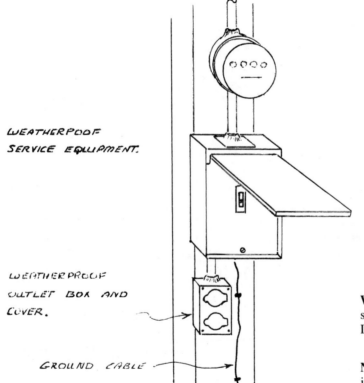

WEATHERPROOF SERVICE EQUIPMENT.

WEATHERPROOF OUTLET BOX AND COVER.

GROUND CABLE

Weatherproof Type – It is better than standard equipment in a wooden enclosure. It is also much simpler to install.

Note – Use an FS outlet box (this is a cast iron box suitable for use outdoors) and spring-loaded, gasketed cover plate over the receptacle as shown. See also rule 26-706.

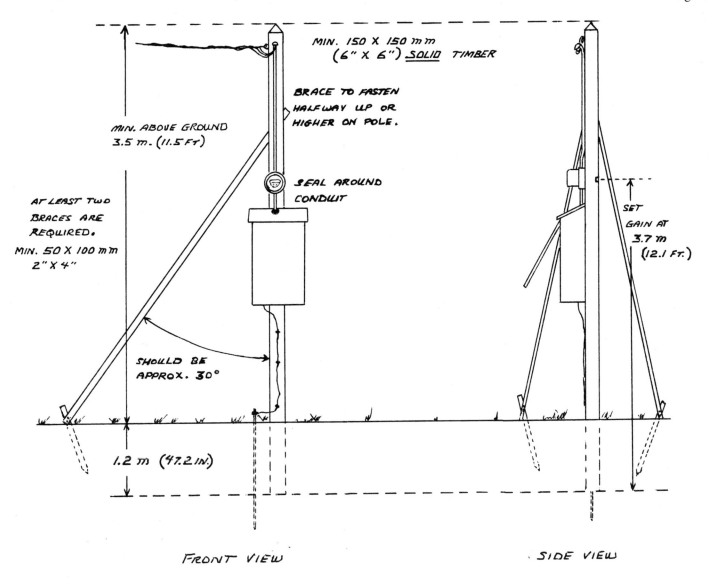

MIN. 150 X 150 mm
(6" X 6") <u>SOLID</u> TIMBER

BRACE TO FASTEN
HALF WAY UP OR
HIGHER ON POLE.

MIN. ABOVE GROUND
3.5 m. (11.5 FT)

SEAL AROUND
CONDUIT

AT LEAST TWO
BRACES ARE
REQUIRED.
MIN. 50 X 100 mm
2" X 4"

SET
GAIN AT
3.7 m
(12.1 FT.)

SHOULD BE
APPROX. 30°

1.2 m (47.2 IN.)

FRONT VIEW   SIDE VIEW

(f) Receptacles

(i)   **120 Volt Receptacles** − A 2 wire, 120 volt service would have a single pole circuit. It could serve one 120 volt plug receptacle.

(ii)   **A 3 Wire, 120/240 Volt Service** would have a 2-pole sircuit breaker. It could serve two 120 volt plug receptacles.

(iii)   **240 Volt Receptacles** − Whenever a 240 volt plug outlet is required, in addition to a 120 volt outlet, you must install a branch circuit panel. A combination circuit breaker panel is the best way out of this awkward requirement.

(g) Grounding

(i)   **Cable** − must be of copper. Where the service is 100 amp. or less the grounding conductor may be #8 BX, #4 bare or even #6 bare copper if not subject to mechanical damage. See also page 34 for more detailed information.

(ii)   **Ground Rods** − Minimum size required.
Copper rods ....½ inch by 1.8 m. (70.9 in.)
Solid iron rod ....⅝ inch by 1.8 m. (70.9 in.)

Note − Use solid rods − pipe is not approved any longer. Rule 10-702.

(iii)   **How Many Rods?** - In most localities 2 rods driven 1.8 m . (approx. 6 ft.) apart, are required. In others you may need more to do the job adequately.

22. PRIVATE GARAGE & FARM BUILDINGS

(a) Overhead Supply Lines

(i) **Insulation of Wire** − Rule 12-302 − Conductors must have weatherproof insulation. Triplex cable is normally used today. Rule 12-318.

(ii) **Elevation of Wire** − Rule 12-304 − Overhead lines must be out of reach, out of harm's way and according to this rule, be at least 4.5 m. (14.8 ft.) above ground. This is obviously not obtainable or necessary in every case, however, before proceeding with anything less than 4.5 m. (14.8 ft.) you should check with your Inspector.

(iii) **Roof Crossing** − Rule 12-312 − Conductors shall not be carried over buildings without special permission and work shall not begin until the plans and specifications for the work are approved by the Inspection department. You might as well know it now, special permission to cross a roof is not easily obtainable.

(iv) **Triplex Type Cable** - Rule 12-318 - A single 15 amp. branch circuit may be run to a building as shown below. The simplist method is to use a triplex cable. This consists of two insulated conductors wrapped around a bare messenger cable. The bare messenger, in the case of a 15 amp. circuit, becomes the grounding conductor between the two buildings.

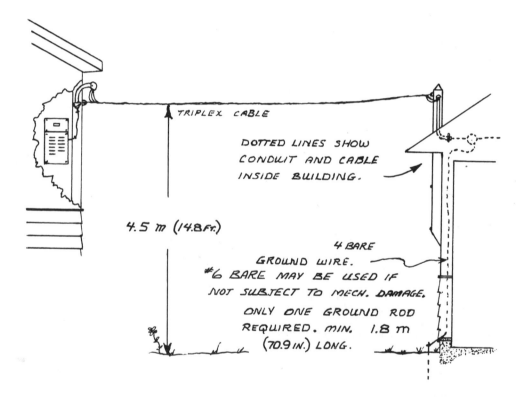

Two 15 amp. circuits may be run overhead as shown but if more circuits are needed a sub-panel is required in the out-buildings.

(v) **Grounding** − Rule 10-208 − Neutral must be grounded at each building which has two circuits or which houses livestock. This grounding conductor is usually #4 bare copper conductor. A #6 conductor may be used if it is not subject to mechanical damage, rule 10-806. The connection may be made in the junction box. Do not use solder for this connection. Normally, only one ground rod is required for each sub-service.

(b) Underground Supply Lines − Rule 12-012 & Bu~~l.~~

Cable Type − is NMWU − table 19 (This is the same a~~s~~
the new code.)

Cable Size − is #14 but for long runs, above 15 m. (50 ft.~~)~~

Cable Depth - 600 mm (23.6 in.) under pedestrian only area.
- 900 mm (35.4 in.) under vehicular traffic areas.

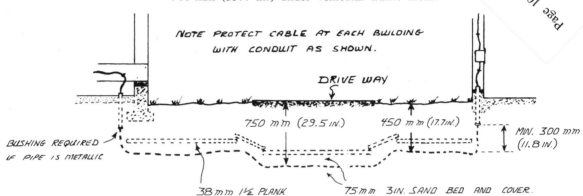

NOTE PROTECT CABLE AT EACH BUILDING
WITH CONDUIT AS SHOWN.

DRIVE WAY

750 mm (29.5 in.)   450 mm (17.7 in.)

MIN. 300 mm
(11.8 in.)

BUSHING REQUIRED
IF PIPE IS METALLIC

38 mm 1½ PLANK   75 mm 3 IN. SAND BED AND COVER.

Note - When a 1½ in. thick plank is laid on the sand above the cable or where the NMWU cable is in a polyethylene pipe, the above depths may be reduced by 6 in. in each case as noted in the illustration.

Cable Protection − Conduit should extend into the trench as shown and cables underground should be protected as follows:

75 mm(3 in.) of sand below cable
75 mm(3 in.) of sand above cable.
38 mm(1½ in.) **plank** above the sand. (Not nominal but actual thickness).

Polyethylene pipe, certified for 50 PSI working pressure, may be used for the **underground portion** only. The riser at each end must be either rigid PVC or rigid metal conduit, not EMT. Bulletin 12-2-0(3)

(c) SUB−PANELS - in a garage or similar building.

Where the load in the garage or other separate building requires more than two 15 amp. circuits, or where you wish to provide for future load additions, a sub-panel may be installed.

Sizes - Where plug outlets are used to supply power tools in a private garage or workshop it is recognized that there will normally be only one man working these tools at any one time. Therefore, even if you have a number of large power tools it is unlikely that more than one tool would be used at any one time. For this reason, when we are calculating the feeder size for this panel, we need to concern ourselves with only one machine, the one with the largest electrical load.

#10 Sub-Feeder - If there is no fixed electrical heating load and no electric welder load a #10 NMD-90 (copper) cable would be sufficient. This cable could supply 30 ampere load at 240 volts. It could supply a 1½ HP power tool at 240 volts, one circuit for lighting and one for plug outlets. The panel should be large enough for present loads plus some reserve capacity for future load additions.

Power Saw

Drill Press

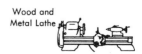
Wood and
Metal Lathe

LOADS - such as welders or fixed el;ectric heaters would require more power and therefore a ~~~ger cable. A #8 NMWU (copper) cable will supply 40 amperes at 240 volts. This is large enough to supply a small private garage type welder, one circuit for lighting and one or more circuits for plug outlets. If the full load current of the welder was say 20 amps, then the circuit breaker supplying the 40 ampere NMWU sub-feeder cable could be as high as 60 amperes. Obviously, the load may not be greater than 40 amperes on this 40 ampere cable but because the biggest load is either a welder load or a motor load the code permits the ampere rating of the main supply breaker to be greater than the cable rating.

WOODWORKING SHOP - This 40 ampere NMWU copper feeder cable supplied with a 60 ampere circuit breaker in the main panel could serve 3 HP 240 volt motor. There would be sufficient capacity left to supply garage lighting and a number of branch circuits for plug outlets.

THE BIG ONE - A #6 NMWU (copper) feeder to a garage or workshop is better but it may be more than is necessary in most cases. If you have an unusually large load, or the length of this feeder to the 2nd building is say 80 ft or more, you should consult your local Electrical Inspector for advice.

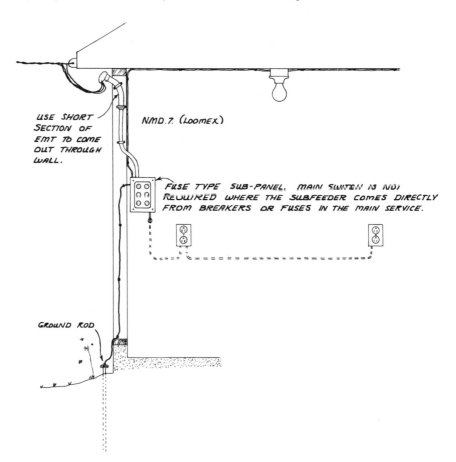

Grounding – Rule 10-208 – Neutral must be grounded at each building which has 2 circuits or which houses livestock. This grounding conductor is usually a #4 bare. A #6 ground conductor may be used if it is not subject to mechanical damage, rule 10-806. The connection may be made in a junction box as shown where only one or two circuits are brought into this building. Do not use solder for this connection. Where the sub-feeder supplies a branch circuit panel in the 2nd building the neutral must be connected to ground in the panel.

Ground Rods - Normally, only one ground rod is required for each sub-service panel in a separate building.

23.   DUPLEX DWELLINGS

(a)   Type of Service − Rule 6-200

> **(i)   Separate Service Conductors** − Rule 6-100(3) − Duplex dwellings may be regarded as two entirely separate buildings. Each half may be served with a separate service pipe, meter and panel and all the instructions for such services would be exactly the same as that given in the appropriate sections in this book for a single family residence.
>
> **Note** − The two entrance caps **must be located close together** so that only one Hydro service drop is required.

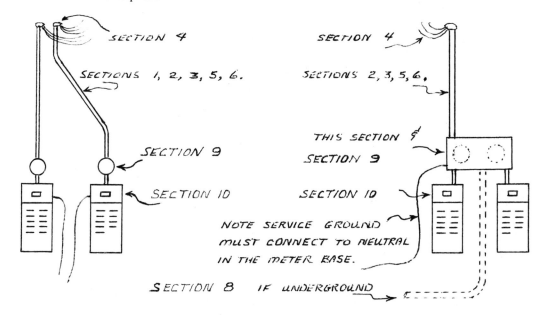

> **(ii)   Common Service Conductors** − Rule 6-200 − This rule has been revised to permit a two-gang meter base to be used without a main switch preceding it in duplex occupancies as shown.
>
> **Note** − The main service conductor must be large enough to carry **100%** of the **sum** of the two sub-feeders. It is not correct to apply the 65% demand factor given in rule 8-202(3). This demand factor may be applied **only** to services which **do have a main service switch**. See sample calculation.

(b)   Calculation

If both halves of the duplex are to be served from a common service the size of these conductors should be as follows:

Sample Calculation − Identical load in each suite.

Basic Load 102.2 m² (1100 sq.ft.) floor area

First 90 m² (968.4 sq.ft.)	5000 watts
Next 12.23 m² (131.6 sq.ft.)	1000 watts
10 kw. range	6000 watts
4 kw. dryer	1000 watts
3 kw. water heater	750 watts
Electric heating (assume 7 kw.)	7000 watts
TOTAL	20750 watts

$$\frac{20750}{240} = 86.5 \text{ amps}$$

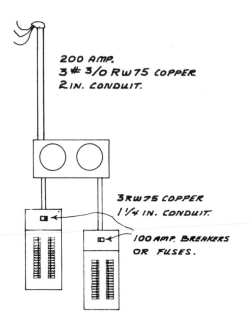

200 AMP.
3 # 3/0 RW75 COPPER
2 IN. CONDUIT.

3 RW75 COPPER
1 1/4 IN. CONDUIT.

100 AMP. BREAKERS
OR FUSES.

Each suite requires —

100 amp. service panel
100 amp. sub-breaker
#3 RW75 copper sub-service wire
1¼ in. sub-service conduit

Main Service

To determine main service size, add the ratings of the two breakers — not the calculated load but the sub-service breaker ratings. See amended rule 6-200. In this case it is 100 + 100 = 200 amp.

(c)   Metering and Service Conductors

Normally the suite service can be installed within a few feet of the meter base, as shown above, so that the total length of the main service plus the longest run to the suite service equipment does not exceed 6 m. (19.7 ft.). In general, **two factors** must be considered when installing this type of service equipment.

(i)   The total length of the service conductor **inside** the building (measured from the point where it enters the building to where it connects to the service switch) may not exceed 6 m. (19.7 ft.) Bulletin 6-4-0(2).

The excess length may be run on the **outside** surface of the building, or in, or under the concrete floor as shown. Note a grounding conductor is required if run under the floor slab. If EMT is used, it should be **in the concrete floor**, it may not be under it. Don't forget to bond the meter base by connecting the neutral conductor to the bonding terminal in the meter base. The EMT run between the service panel and the meter base is not considered adequate bond when in a concrete slab.

(ii)   The length of the sub-service conductors, measured from the meter base to the sub-service panel, may not be more than 7.5 m. (24.6 ft.) unless the sub-feeder is the same size as the main service conductors. Rule 14-100(c).

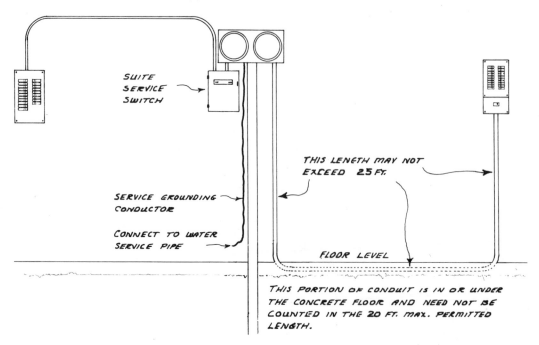

SUITE
SERVICE
SWITCH

THIS LENGTH MAY NOT
EXCEED 25 FT.

SERVICE GROUNDING
CONDUCTOR

CONNECT TO WATER
SERVICE PIPE

FLOOR LEVEL

THIS PORTION OF CONDUIT IS IN OR UNDER
THE CONCRETE FLOOR AND NEED NOT BE
COUNTED IN THE 20 FT. MAX. PERMITTED
LENGTH.

Two alternative methods in overcoming these problems are shown above. The **left hand** suite is served with a sub-service switch located at the meter base. This switch or breaker should be weatherproof type and face **outdoors** so that the tenant in the suite served has access to it at all times. See also Rule 26-440. Check with your Inspector for special permission before locating this switch outdoors. The sub-feeder can then be as long as required in excess of 7.5 m. (24.6 ft.).

The **right hand** suite service does not have a sub-service switch or breaker at the meter base and therefore its length, if it is inside the building, plus that portion of the main service conduit which is within the building, must not exceed 6 m. (19.7 ft.). The Fig. shows a portion of the conduit **in** the concrete floor, this portion may be subtracted from the length of the sub-feeder, reducing the total length to 6 m. (19.7 ft.). In the same way conduit may be run on the outside surface of the building thereby reducing the length indoors to 6 m. (19.7 ft.) as required.

(d) Service Equipment

Where a 2−gang meter base is used the service equipment in each suite would be the same as if each suite were a separate building. A combination fuse or breaker panel is most often used in each suite.

(e) Service Grounding

Where separate service conductors are installed for each suite, each service shall be separately grounded as described under "Grounding" page 34 in this book.

Where a **two−headed** meter base is used, the service ground shall connect to the neutral bus **in the meter base.**

(i) Size of Grounding Conductor − may be determined from the table, page 5 in this book.

Note − that the size of this grounding conductor is related to the current carrying capacity of the **main service conductor.**

24. REWIRING AN EXISTING HOUSE

(a) **Electrical Service Panel** – Bulletin 0-2-0

Old Panel - if you are adding load to an existing panel in an old house but have no more breaker or fuse spaces you will need to install an additional sub panel and feed it from breakers in the existing panel. Before you do this, check the existing service equipment if adequate to supply the new load. If it is adequate the additional panel could be located close the existing old panel. There is a reason for suggesting this location. You will need two circuit breaker spaces for the feeder to the new panel. If there are no more spaces reroute two existing circuits from the old to the new panel. This will free two breaker spaces for the sub-feeder breakers.

Change Service panel - This will cost a bit more but it may be the only solution if the old stuff is too small. Don't forget that if you change the panel you must upgrade the whole service, not the branch circuit wiring but the service. The reason for this is the new service may require larger conductors, conduit, meter base and grounding. It may also be necessary to find a more acceptable location for the new panel, meter base or service entrance cap. It may also be that all of these items are satisfactory and all that is needed is to replace the old panel with a larger one.

All this may sound expensive and indeed may be but don't forget this is the most important part of your installation. This is what protects all the circuits in the house and this is where that enormous hydro electric capacity is limited to a safe value. To compromise here is to compromise with minimum safety.

Caution - Even if it looks harmless, Don't take chances. Before any work is begun you should make sure that that part of the system you will be working on is, in fact, not energized.

If you are changing your service equipment have Hydro crew disconnect your service before you begin work.

Where a service has been changed the Inspector will usually check for:

- **Entrance cap** – Re: height and location, page 12.

- **Size of Service Conduit & Conductors** – This may have been large enough at one time but may be too small now. See under "Service Size", page 1.

- **Meter Location etc.** – Size of opening? Accessibility? etc. page 26.

- **New Panel** – Must comply with new code re: ampacity, number of circuit positions and number of 2–pole positions available for 240 volt and 3 wire circuits, page 28.

- **Grounding** – Size of conductor, condition of run, connected to old abandoned water service? Must comply with current regulations, see page 34.

- **Bonding** – Older houses may have metal waste pipe system which may not have been bonded. In that case the code requires a bonding connection between the metal waste piping and the nearest cold water pipe.

(b) **Branch Circuit Wiring**

The Inspector will not normally require the existing finished areas to be rewired except as may be necessary for minimum safety. He will, however, require upgrading of branch circuit wiring where the walls have been opened to make other structural revisions or additions to the house.
He has the knowledge and the experience to guide him in his assessment of your installation. He will ask for minimum changes to the existing wiring to make your home reasonably safe. The fact is – it's your safety he is concerned about.

Additions To House. - All new wiring in the new addition must comply with the current regulations. The information on branch circuit wiring given in this book does apply to the additional wiring.
Caution - Before entering the service panel make sure the main switch is in the "off" position.

Electrical Permit – make sure your electrical permit is adequate to cover the work done.

25. MOBILE HOMES

(a) C.S.A. Marking — Bulletin 2—9—0

The mobile unit must have a C.S.A. label. If it does not have that label you are in deep trouble. Older units may not have this certification label. Sometimes it is lost in a move or for one reason or another it is gone. In that case, check with your Inspector. Years ago the Chinese man who did my shirts would say, "No ticky, no laundry". It's like that with the C.S.A. label — no label, no approval for connection.

(b) Electrical Permit — Bulletin 72-2-0

An electrical permit must be obtained before any electrical work is done.

> **Note** — If this mobile unit is on private property and you are personally going to occupy it, you are usually permitted to obtain a permit.
>
> If this mobile unit is to be occupied by someone in your immediate family, you are usually permitted to obtain an electrical permit.
>
> If this unit is for rental purposes to someone other than the immediate family then the wiring must be installed by an electrical contractor.
>
> If this unit is to be connected in a mobile home park the work must be done by a certified electrical contractor. The owner would not be permitted to do this work nor to take out a permit.

(c) Service Size — Rule 72-102(1)amended.

Mobile homes are treated the same as a single family dwelling as far as service ampacity is concerned. See the table on page 5 for quick sizing of service equipment.

Rules 70-110, 8—200

Floor area — less than 80 m² (861 sq.ft.)

The normal load will be something like this.

Basic	5000 watts
Range — (12 kw. range)	6000 watts
Water heater - (3 kw tank)	750 watts
Dryer — (4 kw. unit)	1000 watts
Quick Steam Tap — (500 watts)	0 watts
Furnace — (gas or oil)	0 watts
Freezer	0 watts
Dishwasher	0 watts
Fridge	0 watts
Total =	**12750 watts**

$$\frac{12750}{240} = 53.1 \text{ amps.}$$

The code requires a 60 amp. service for this load.

Note — It really does not matter if the range, dryer, water heater and furnace are **all gas** — the fact is, the minimum service size is still 60 amp. for **any size** floor area **up to 80 m².**

Floor Area − 80 m² or larger (861 sq.ft.)

100 amps − This is the minimum size acceptable by code rules.

Unfortunately, the rules make no distinction between a single family house and a mobile home. The same rules used to determine the size of a service in a house are also applied in determining the size of service in a mobile home.

We all know that the calculated load in this unit is much less than 100 amp. The extra service ampacity is usually intended for **future** load changes. In single family houses there is always a possibility of finishing a basement, adding a sauna or large power vacuum etc. In a mobile home such changes are difficult, very costly and rare. For this reason check with your local Inspector if he will accept a 60 amp. service for this larger mobile unit. (Just don't tell him I sent ya).

(A)   SINGLE UNIT IN MOBILE PARK

(a)   Connection Box in Mobile Home Park

A typical connection box in each lot in a mobile home park.

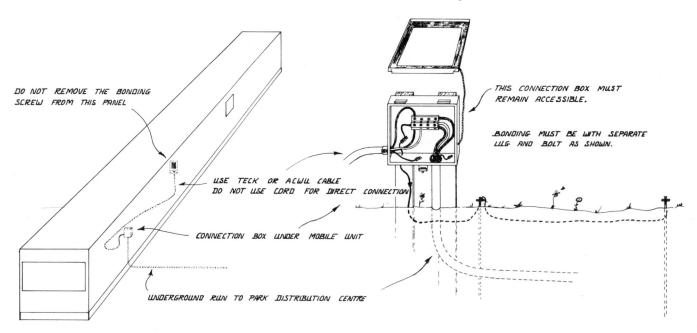

Connection to this box can only be made by a certified electrical contractor. Neither the owner of the mobile unit nor the mobile park operator (or owner) may make this connection **unless** they have a valid Certificate of Competency from the Provincial Government Inspection Department.

An electrical permit must be obtained before connection.

Cable Connector − The cable from the mobile unit must connect to the box with a connector approved for the particular cable you are using.

Conductor Terminations in Box − Watch this carefully − most of the problems are right here.

− Don't skin back too much insulation − only enough to make good connections.

− If the box does not have a terminal strip as shown − use only approved connectors to make the splices − if aluminum conductor is used, this is extremely important.

− **Bonding** − Terminate the grounding conductor in an approved lug which is **separately bolted** to the box. Don't try to use a bolt or screw already used for some other purpose.

− **Clean the Surface** under the bonding lug to ensure a good electrical contact.

(B) SINGLE UNIT ON PRIVATE PROPERTY

(a) Basic Requirements

(i) Permission to Place Mobile Home

More and more of our freedoms are being taken away from us. Before you move a mobile unit onto your own property, it is best to find out first if that would be permitted by local by–law. In some cases you will be required to produce some kind of proof of approval from the local authorities before the Electrical Inspection department will issue an electrical permit for connection.

(ii) Consult Hydro – Rules 6-210 & 6-114(a)

Before any work is done the power utility should be consulted to determine which pole service will be from.

(b) Connection Methods

There are several connection methods you may choose from – each has it's problems and pitfalls.

DIP SERVICE

As shown below, only the meter is on the pole. The service conductors dip underground to a point under the panel where they rise and enter the service box in a mobile unit. This means the service conductors **do not** have fuse protection until they enter the panel. It means there is no quick easy shut-off, except by removal of the meter when the moving truck arrives. This method does **not** require special permission but in **my view** this is the one method which should require special permission for mobile homes.

(c) DIP SERVICE   – Special permission not
required for this connection.

Note - Meter only on service pole.

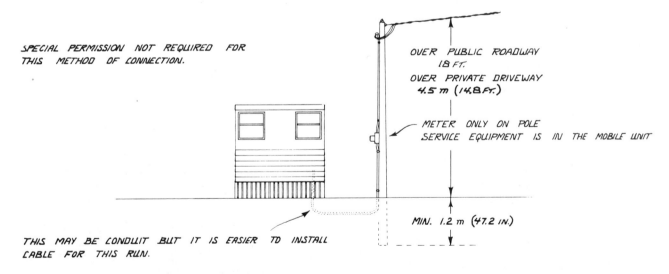

SPECIAL PERMISSION NOT REQUIRED FOR THIS METHOD OF CONNECTION.

OVER PUBLIC ROADWAY 18 FT.
OVER PRIVATE DRIVEWAY 4.5 m (14.8 FT.)

METER ONLY ON POLE SERVICE EQUIPMENT IS IN THE MOBILE UNIT

MIN. 1.2 m (47.2 IN.)

THIS MAY BE CONDUIT BUT IT IS EASIER TO INSTALL CABLE FOR THIS RUN.

REMEMBER, THIS IS A SERVICE CABLE IN THIS CASE AND THEREFORE MUCH MORE CARE MUST BE TAKEN WHEN INSTALLING IT. MAXIMUM LENGTH PERMITTED UNDER THE MOBILE UNIT IS 20 FT. (6 m) UNLESS THE CABLE IS BURIED. SEE BULLETIN 6-2-0.

(d) <u>**Mast on Mobile Unit**</u>

Special permission is not required for this method of service to a mobile unit.

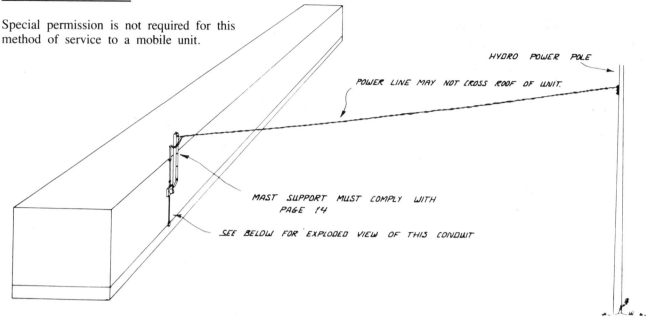

HYDRO POWER POLE

POWER LINE MAY NOT CROSS ROOF OF UNIT.

MAST SUPPORT MUST COMPLY WITH PAGE 14

SEE BELOW FOR EXPLODED VIEW OF THIS CONDUIT

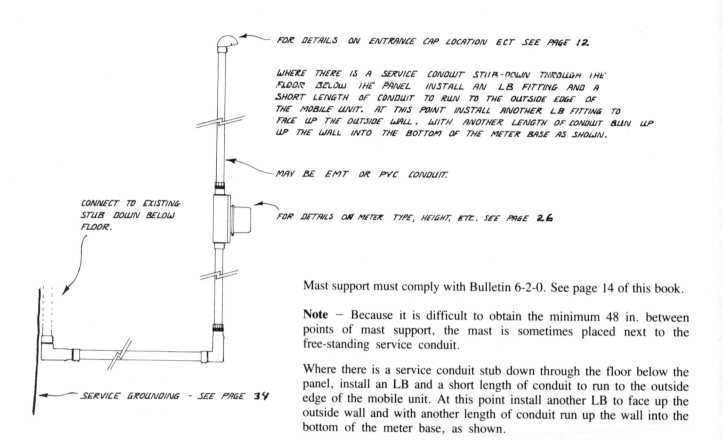

FOR DETAILS ON ENTRANCE CAP LOCATION ECT SEE PAGE 12.

WHERE THERE IS A SERVICE CONDUIT STUB-DOWN THROUGH THE FLOOR BELOW THE PANEL INSTALL AN LB FITTING AND A SHORT LENGTH OF CONDUIT TO RUN TO THE OUTSIDE EDGE OF THE MOBILE UNIT. AT THIS POINT INSTALL ANOTHER LB FITTING TO FACE UP THE OUTSIDE WALL. WITH ANOTHER LENGTH OF CONDUIT RUN UP UP THE WALL INTO THE BOTTOM OF THE METER BASE AS SHOWN.

MAY BE EMT OR PVC CONDUIT.

CONNECT TO EXISTING STUB DOWN BELOW FLOOR.

FOR DETAILS ON METER TYPE, HEIGHT, ETC. SEE PAGE 26

Mast support must comply with Bulletin 6-2-0. See page 14 of this book.

Note − Because it is difficult to obtain the minimum 48 in. between points of mast support, the mast is sometimes placed next to the free-standing service conduit.

Where there is a service conduit stub down through the floor below the panel, install an LB and a short length of conduit to run to the outside edge of the mobile unit. At this point install another LB to face up the outside wall and with another length of conduit run up the wall into the bottom of the meter base, as shown.

SERVICE GROUNDING − SEE PAGE 34

(e) <u>**Where a Tall Mast is Required**</u>

Where the line to ground clearance required is more than can be obtained from a standard 30 in. high mast, a longer 6 in. by 6 in. or larger, mast may be used. This mast must be **securely fastened** to the mobile unit. If this is not done the service conduit could break.

(f) Pole Service – By SPECIAL PERMISSION ONLY

This is an outdoor service and Bulletin 6-6-0(1) says special permission is required for such an installation. Special permission for these installations is usually easy to obtain, but ask first. Service ampacity is based on Rule 70-110 which is the same as for a house of similar size. See table on page 5.

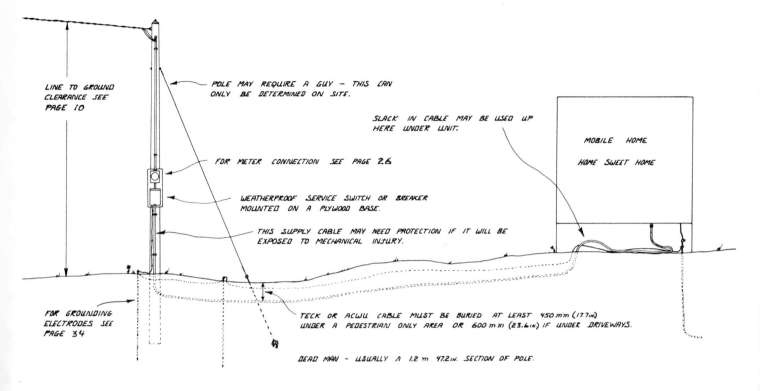

LINE TO GROUND CLEARANCE SEE PAGE 10

POLE MAY REQUIRE A GUY – THIS CAN ONLY BE DETERMINED ON SITE.

SLACK IN CABLE MAY BE USED UP HERE UNDER UNIT.

MOBILE HOME

HOME SWEET HOME

FOR METER CONNECTION SEE PAGE 2.6

WEATHERPROOF SERVICE SWITCH OR BREAKER MOUNTED ON A PLYWOOD BASE.

THIS SUPPLY CABLE MAY NEED PROTECTION IF IT WILL BE EXPOSED TO MECHANICAL INJURY.

FOR GROUNDING ELECTRODES SEE PAGE 34

TECK OR ACWU CABLE MUST BE BURIED AT LEAST 450 mm (17.7 in.) UNDER A PEDESTRIAN ONLY AREA OR 600 mm (23.6 in.) IF UNDER DRIVEWAYS.

DEAD MAN – USUALLY A 1.2 m (47.2 in.) SECTION OF POLE.

Grounding – Use two 1800 mm. (6 ft.) ground rods and connect to the water service pipe under the unit. See under **Grounding** page 34 for detailed information.

Cable Types – ACWU, TECK and Corflex may be used. NMW10 may also be used when provided with adequate mechanical protection – not recommended for this application.

Service – See index for detailed list of requirements.

(g) Cable Termination in Panel

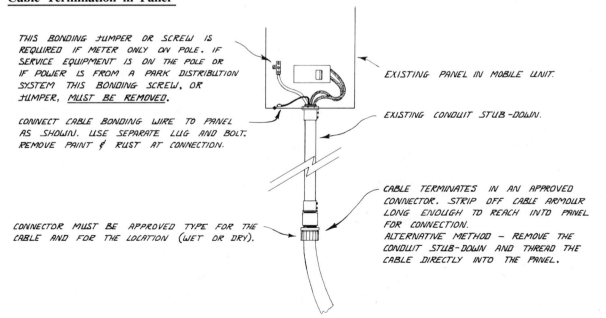

THIS BONDING JUMPER OR SCREW IS REQUIRED IF METER ONLY ON POLE. IF SERVICE EQUIPMENT IS ON THE POLE OR IF POWER IS FROM A PARK DISTRIBUTION SYSTEM THIS BONDING SCREW, OR JUMPER, MUST BE REMOVED.

CONNECT CABLE BONDING WIRE TO PANEL AS SHOWN. USE SEPARATE LUG AND BOLT. REMOVE PAINT & RUST AT CONNECTION.

CONNECTOR MUST BE APPROVED TYPE FOR THE CABLE AND FOR THE LOCATION (WET OR DRY).

EXISTING PANEL IN MOBILE UNIT.

EXISTING CONDUIT STUB-DOWN.

CABLE TERMINATES IN AN APPROVED CONNECTOR. STRIP OFF CABLE ARMOUR LONG ENOUGH TO REACH INTO PANEL FOR CONNECTION.
ALTERNATIVE METHOD – REMOVE THE CONDUIT STUB-DOWN AND THREAD THE CABLE DIRECTLY INTO THE PANEL.

(h) **Pole Location on Property**

This is very important — consider the following:

(i) **Near Connection Point**

The pole should be (not must be) located near the point of service connection on the mobile unit. The length of your existing supply cable will often determine this.

(ii) **Length of Hydro Lines Required**

Note the Hydro power pole location. They will usually run 30 m (98 ft.) onto your property without additional fee. Beyond this length they may be into your wallet for more money. Long runs, more than 30 m. (98 ft.) may also require additional poles and this is at your expense, usually.

(iii) **Crossing**

— **Public Roadway**

You may not have a choice. If the Hydro line is on the other side of the road you must cross the road with the line. Clearance required is 5.5 m. (18 ft.) **minimum** above roadway. It may require a long pole to do this.

— **Driveways**

Avoid crossing driveways if possible. If you must cross, a minimum line to ground clearance is 4 m. (13 ft.) above a driveway. This is generally considered the minimum height even if there is no garage or carport, only a driveway.

— **Roof**

No! No! No! — you must not cross the roof of any building including the roof of the mobile unit. Locate the pole so as to avoid it.

(i) **Pole Requirements**

Types — Cedar, fir, lodgepole pine are usually acceptable. If you go into the woods to cut down a tree to make a pole, observe the following picky points:

1 — Make sure it is straight and has the correct dimensions — see below under 'length'.

2 — Remove all branches, leaving a smooth surface.

3 — Remove all bark.

4 — Cut a gain mark 3.7 m. (12.1 in.) from butt, as shown below.

5 — Apply an effective treatment to butt ends to retard rotting.

Note — It may be possible to use a sawn timber instead of a round pole. It is not recommended and before you try it, check with your Inspector.

Size — Bulletin 72-2-0 says it must be a minimum Class 6. This means it must be:

1 — **Minimum** 17 inches **circumference** at the top of the pole. This is 5.4 in.diameter. This is minimum, it may be larger.

2 — **Minimum** 21 inches **circumference** at 6 ft. from the butt end.

These are the minimum dimensions, no matter how long the pole needs to be to provide proper line clearance.

Length — Two factors must be considered.

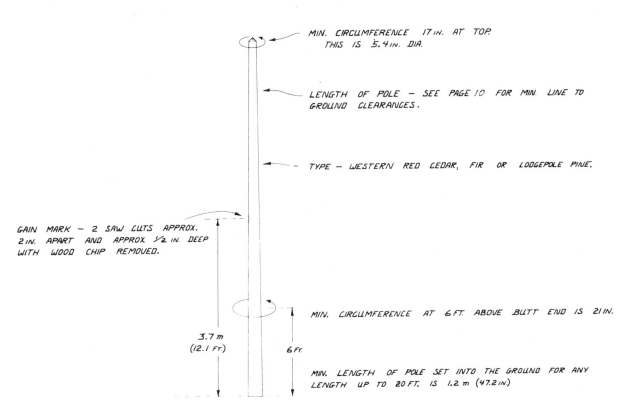

MIN. CIRCUMFERENCE 17 IN. AT TOP.
THIS IS 5.4 IN. DIA.

LENGTH OF POLE — SEE PAGE 10 FOR MIN. LINE TO GROUND CLEARANCES.

TYPE — WESTERN RED CEDAR, FIR OR LODGEPOLE PINE.

GAIN MARK — 2 SAW CUTS APPROX. 2 IN. APART AND APPROX ½ IN. DEEP WITH WOOD CHIP REMOVED.

MIN. CIRCUMFERENCE AT 6 FT. ABOVE BUTT END IS 21 IN.

3.7 m (12.1 FT.)

6 FT.

MIN. LENGTH OF POLE SET INTO THE GROUND FOR ANY LENGTH UP TO 20 FT. IS 1.2 m (47.2 IN.)

1 — Length of pole **above** ground. This is simply line to ground clearances given on page 10. Add to this:

2 — Length of pole **set into the ground**. In most cases this is 1.2 m. (47.2 in.). Where the pole length **above ground** must be greater than 6 m. (19.7 ft.) the length of the pole set into the ground must be increased.

Guy Lines — When Required? This must be determined on site. A very rough thumb rule is as follows:

If the length (of pole above ground) is 4 m (13.1 ft.) or less and the length of span for the Hydro lines is say 10 m. (59 ft.) a guy is very likely **not** required. If the dimensions are greater than these, it is very likely you will need to guy the pole.

— **Type of Guy Wire** — must be galvinized cable. Do not try to use ordinary wire rope or clothes line cable.

— **Size** — ¼ in. guy wire would be sufficient in most cases.

— **Dead Man** — This is usually a 4 ft. length of log buried to the same depth as the pole setting. Use a long anchor bolt as shown in the diagram.

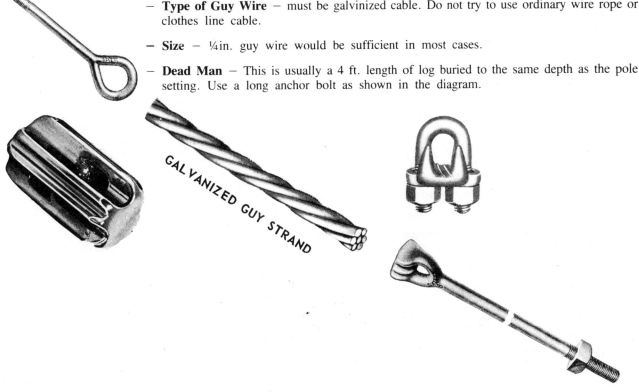

GALVANIZED GUY STRAND

26. EXAMINATIONS for CERTIFICATION

In the official examination you are not permitted to use your own code book or bulletin book. The examiner will supply unmarked copies of these books to you. He will also supply writing paper for your calculations.

The time allowed for the exam is 3½ hours. Use all of it. This is not a test to determine who finishes first but who finishes best.

Don't guess where True or False answers are required. A penalty is assessed for each incorrect answer. Therefore, you lose not only the marks for the question but also an equal mark as a penalty.

The theory behind this is that if you knew the correct answer, you would have given it , but since you gave an incorrect answer you must have have been guessing. Therefore, if you don't know the correct answer, leave it blank.

TYPICAL EXAMINATION QUESTIONS

SECTION 1   TRUE or FALSE   True   False

Allow 2 points for each correct answer and subtract 2 points for each incorrect answer.

1. A CSA enclosure 3 may be used indoors where subject to drops of falling liquid due to heavy condensation ....

2. A standard duplex receptacle may be installed in a bathroom provided it is supplied with a ground fault type circuit interrupter.

3. The neutral must be bonded to the meter base in every case without exception...

4. The plug outlet on the bathroom light fixture is acceptable to the code for the bathroom plug............................

5. A diesel fuel pump at a service station is considered less hazardous than a gasoline fuel pump ....

6. The grounding conductor running around a pool must connect to the reinforcing steel of the pool in at least 3 equally spaced points around the pool...

7. The metal supply conduit to the deck box for an underwater swimming pool light fixture may be used to ground the fixture

8. The rules permit the G.F.C.I. type receptacle in the bathroom to also serve the outdoor plug outlet ....

9. A splitter box is required in every case where a tap conductor is connected to a larger conductor.........................

10. The electrical code specifically states that where two or more smoke alarms are installed they shall be interconnected to sound together ....

11. There is no limit to the length of service conduit if it is run on the outside surface of the building......................

12. A grounding conductor is not required in seal-tight flex provided it is smaller than 1 inch.................................

13. The code does not require the secondary of a 24 volt class II transformer to be grounded when the primary is 120 volts .

14. Plug outlets may be located between 60 in.(1.5 m) and 118 in.(3 m) of the inside wall of a swimming pool provided they are protected with a G.F.C.I. of the class A type..

15. TWH conductor is rated for 75 C and therefore may be used in conduit for fire alarm system wiring ....

16. Conductors of any size or colour may be painted white and used for neutral conductors except in the case of ser-vice conductors ....

17. The disconnect for a hoist must be accessible from the ground or from the floor below the hoist.........................

18. The plug outlet for the door opener in a garage may be supplied with a garage lighting circuit ....

19. A telephone jack, if located in a bathroom, must be at least 1.2m from a tub or shower.....................................

20. Electrical metallic tubing must be securely fastened in place within 3 ft. of each outlet box, junction box, cabinet or fitting

21. A #4 conductor could not carry any current at all in an ambient temperature of 60 C...

22. Underground wiring to the dispensing pumps at a gas station must conform to code requirements for Class 1. Div. 2 hazardous location wiring methods ....

23. If the pump and hot tub are at least 3 m apart G.F.I. protection is not required...

24. A circuit supplying a combination heat lamp (maximum rating 300 watts) and exhaust fan may also supply other outlets..

25. Sectional boxes are now approved for use embedded in concrete..

26. Set screw type EMT couplings and connectors may be used underground provided the conduit is not buried below permanent moisture level...

27. An electrical permit is required for all small jobs such as a furnace, range or dryer connection .... _____ _____

28. The wiring for fire alarm systems may not be drawn into conduits used for other circuits. They must be kept entirely separated except at point of supply.. _____ _____

29. It is the responsibility of the Electrical Contractor to ensure that all the electrical equipment he connects has been properly certified by CSA or by the BC Government Safety Inspection Service.. _____ _____

30. The service conductors for a 60 amp. service in Prince George may be #6 TW provided the demand load is not more than 55 amp.. _____ _____

31. For a single family dwelling, all outdoor plug receptacles, which are accessible from grade level, must be supplied with a circuit used for no other purpose .... _____ _____

SECTION TWO   —   FILL IN THE BLANK SPACES.

Each question is worth 2 points.

1. Minimum permissible radius of teck cable bends is ____ the internal diameter of the cable.

2. Junction boxes may be installed in attics, ceiling spaces or crawl spaces provided the head room, vertical clearance, is _____ .

3. The maximum permissible load on a sign circuit is ____%.

4. Where conduit is buried underground it shall be at least _____ below the surface where it is subject to vehicular traffic and _____ where not subject to vehicular traffic.

5. The rated secondary open circuit voltage of a sign transformer shall not exceed _____ volts.

6. Where NMS cable is run through studs, joists or similar wooden members, the outer surface of the cable shall be kept at least _____ from the nailing edges of wooden members or be protected.

7. Where light fixtures are mounted less than _____ above the floor they must be guarded or be flexible.

8. The maximum number of light or plug outlets permitted on a circuit is _____.

9. The minimum wiring method for Class I, Division I location is ____.

10. The maximum length of a #14 TW tap from a 30 amp. branch circuit for heating is ____.

11. Outlet boxes must be set flush with the surface finish except that in the case where the finish is non-combustible type, the box may be set back ____.

12. The minimum size bonding conductor for a spa is _____.

13. The maximum heating load that may be connected to a 30 amp. 240 volt branch circuit breaker in a residence is ____ watts.

14. The service entrance cap shall be so located that open conductors are above windows etc. or not less than ____ from windows or similar openings.

15. The minimum distance between an electrical meter and a gas meter is _____.

16. Meter bases shall be installed so that they are not more than ____ not less than ____ from grade level to center of base.

17. The service equipment shall be installed so that it is approximately _____ from the floor to the center of the equipment but in no case shall the lower end be less than _____ above floor level.

18. The conductors used to supply ceiling light outlets shall have an insulation rating of ____ C.

19. The minimum size of copper grounding conductor permitted for a UFER (concrete encased electrode) grounding electrode is _____.

20. The maximum current that a #14 NMD7 copper cable, which is rated for 90 degrees C. may carry is _____ amp.

SECTION THREE   ADDITIONAL QUESTIONS

Write your answers on a separate sheet of paper

Marks

2	1.	May the service neutral for a single family dwelling be bare (uninsulated)?
2	2.	May flexible cord be used as a substitute for fixed wiring?
2	3.	What does the term "readily accessible" mean?
5	4.	Calculate the maximum expected expansion in a 12.2 m stright run of 3/4 in. PVC conduit located where the temperature will vary between 115 F to −30 F.
5	5.	What size conduit is required for the following combination of copper conductors; 12 #12TW, 3 #6TW and 3 #10TW.

6. An apartment has 8 suites. The floor area in 4 suites is 45 m²0 (484 sq.ft.). Each has a 9 kw. range, a 3 kw. water heater, a 4 amp. gas furnace. The remaining 4 suites are 79 m² (850 sq.ft.) each and each has a 12 kw. range, 3 kw. water heater, 4 amp gas furnace and a 5 amp 120 volt garburator. The house load consists of one 4 kw. dryer and 1 kw. of light. Electric service is 120/240 volt, single phase.

Calculate the following:

5   a. main service load in amperes.

5   b. small suite feeder load in amperes.

5   c. large suite feeder load in amperes.

5   d. minimum number of branch circuit spaces required by code for   (i)   small suite.

                                                                                   (ii)   large suite.

2   e. main service conductor size required.

2   f. sub-feeder size to small suite.

2   g. sub-feeder size to large suite.

2   h. main service ground.

2   i. may the holder of a C certificate install this service?

10   7   A single family residence has a floor area of 2000 sq. ft. including breakfast room and laundry room. There are two ⅓ hp. 110 volt motors in the basement hobby workshop. There will be a 12KW range, 3KW water heater, 4KW dryer, an 11amp. dish washer and a 3 amp. garburator. Air conditioning is with a 1200VA unit. There are 70 plug outlets and 20 light outlets. There is also a 4KW sauna, 8KW electric heating and a 4KW hot tub heater. Calculate the minimum service size required by code. Service is 120/240 single phase.

8. Calculate the wiring requirements for a 5 hp. single phase, 230 volt totally enclosed, non-ventilated motor with Class B insulation for a saw on a construction project.

2   a. What size wire and conduit is required for this load?

2   b. What size code fuse is required?

2   c. What size overload protection is required?

2   d. What other motor protection does the code require?

2   e. What is the purpose of the protection required by (d)?

2   f. Would #8 TW copper be acceptable if run into the motor terminal box.

5   9.   a. What is emergency lighting?

5   b. Describe fully one method of providing emergency lighting.

5   10. Describe fully how you would install a recessed light fixture.

2   11. Does the code require the nameplate on electrical equipment to remain accessible after instalation?

2   12   a. What is the minimum service cap height permitted by code.

2   b. What is the minimum height of service drop wires over a public roadway?

2   13.   a. When using 3-wire loomex cable, would it be permitted to connect both the black and the red wires in this cable to different breakers in the panel but to the same bus?

2   b. Give a reason for your answer to question (a).

2   14.   a. How large a service may be installed by a Class C Electrical Contractor?

2   b. What is the maximum rating of the overcurrent device for a lighting branch circuit in a residence?

2   c. What is the maximum rating of the overcurrent device for a branch circuit supplying polarized outlets in the kitchen if the wiring is #12 loomex (copper)?

15. You are asked to connect a 46 amp. manually operated transformer type welder which has a duty cycle of 80% in a non-hazardous area in an existing building in Vancouver. The service is 120/240 volt, single phase.

2   a. What is the minimum size copper feeder required by code if TW insulation is used?

2   b. What is the minimum size aluminum feeder required by code if TW insulation is used?

2   c. If this feeder can be concealed within the building structure, will the code permit it to be NMD7 or NMW-90?

2   16.   a. What is an EYS fitting?

2   b. Where is it used?

2   17. When wiring barns or stables may NMD7 cable be used?

18. You are to install the wiring for the lighting and small motors in a machine shop. The service is 120/240 volt, single phase. The building is of frame construction.

2   a. Would the requirements permit NMS cable to be used for lighting and plug outlet wiring in this building?

2   b. Could NMS cable be used to supply the 2 hp. lathe and the 2 hp. compressor motors?

4   19. Two circuits are run side by side but in separate conduits. One is #6 R90 copper, the other is #6 TW. They are both of equal length and both carry full rated current. Which circuit will have the greatest I R loss?

2   20   When connecting end to end mounted fluorescent light fixtures may R90 wire be used?

3   21. What is the maximum I R loss permitted on an emergency circuit?

2   22. Where must the bathroom light switch be placed.